C000230810

BRAVE NEW WILDERNESS

Brave New Wilderness

WILDLIFE IN BRITAIN SINCE
THE INDUSTRIAL REVOLUTION

Gavin Weightman

PHOTOGRAPHS BY MIKE BIRKHEAD

WEIDENFELD AND NICOLSON LONDON
IN ASSOCIATION WITH LONDON WEEKEND TELEVISION LIMITED

CONTENTS

FRONT ENDPAPERS
Chemical factories, Teeside.

HALF-TITLE
Pearl bordered fritilary.

FRONTISPIECE
Flighting ducks.

OPPOSITE
Little owl.

Published in Great Britain by
George Weidenfeld & Nicolson Limited
91 Clapham High Street
London SW4 7TA

ISBN 0 297 81041 3

Printed in Great Britain by
Butler & Tanner Ltd, Frome and London

For Clare, Jack and Kate

Written with Alison Kreps

OPPOSITE *Chinese water deer.*

ACKNOWLEDGEMENTS

Because this study attempts to relate social and economic history to natural history it draws on the specialised knowledge of many disciplines. Without the help and enthusiasm of a great many people it could never have been undertaken. And because the conclusions presented here, on what is for many a very emotive issue, are entirely personal many of those who have offered their time and expertise will not necessarily agree with them. There is in fact a great and understandable fear that if too optimistic a view is given about what has happened in the past it will encourage complacency in the future. That is not the intention of this book. But there is a determination to be truthful, however naive such an approach may appear to be.

Sadly, Mike Birkhead, a zoological mentor over several years, does not share the views expressed in the book. For him, industrialism has been an unmitigated disaster for the natural world. Another mentor, Richard Mabey, who discussed the outline of the book but has not had a chance to see it, will, I hope, go along with some of it. His writing about natural history has always been an inspiration. Jim Lovelock's brilliant work on planetary chemistry has also been very influential.

Oliver Rackham was the source of most wisdom on woodland; Peter Evans and Dan Osborne on seabirds and toxic waste; all those at Great Linford research station on gravel pits; Wynn Wheeler on fish, rivers and canals; David Fowler on acid rain; Bob Bunce on landscape changes; Derek Ratcliffe on the peregrine falcon and many other subjects; Barrie Trinder on industrial history; and the Weald and Downland museum on woodland crafts. John Sheail, Roy Switsur, Norman Moore, Richard Briggs, Ken Smith, Bill and Jean Armstrong, and Keith Bennett, have all been generous with their help. Col. James Baker, Lt. Col. Ian Graham, Col. Collings and Col. Norman Clayden have given invaluable assistance on the wildlife of the military ranges. James Bowskill was kind enough to allow us to join his pheasant shoot, and Joe Cowan invited us to join the Fernie in pursuit of foxes. Phillip Castang very kindly opened the company archives to provide evidence of the trade in live foxes during the nineteenth century.

A great many people, far too numerous to mention, were a tremendous help in pinning down local histories, Paul Miller, who assisted Mike Birkhead on wildlife filming, contributed some useful research, and cameraman Tony Phelps was a mine of information on snakes.

At London Weekend Television, Sarah, Michelle and Mark in the reference library provided wonderful support as always; Sue Richardson not only kept us going but unearthed some valuable information; Jane Hewland got the project going, and many others contributed to the success of the book and the series. A special thanks to Carl Thomson and Patrick McDonnell.

All opinions, and errors, are naturally our own responsibility.

Gavin Weightman

I give my sincere thanks to all the people who helped me with the photographs in this book. Inevitably I will have missed someone out for which I apologise.

Paul Miller, Dave Shale, Ian Gray, Ashely Smith and Jim Chick of the Hawk Conservancy – a great place for a visit – T & A, D. Poyser, Nick Giles and all at the Great Linford Wildfowl Centre, Michael Rosenberg, Alastair MacEwen, Roger Pearson, Nigel Dunstan, Richard Doyle-Davidson of Wentworth Golf Club, and Owen Newman and Basil. Finally I would like to thank Caroline Aitzetmuller for all her invaluable help and support throughout the making of the television series and the book.

Mike Birkhead

OPPOSITE *Greylag Geese.*

INTRODUCTION

Even a sunny winter's day is greeted now with trepidation: it is evidence not of fortune smiling on the world but of a hole in the ozone layer eaten away by invisible particles from aerosol cans, or a sign that greenhouse gases are overheating the planet. The rain itself is eyed warily – it might be acid, not a life force but a poison. There has been such an air of doom in recent years about the dangers of climatic change brought on by the forces of industrialism that it feels trite to take an interest in what has happened to wild plants and animals in Britain over the past two centuries. With such a dismal forecast for the future, who is worried about the history?

Whatever its scientific justification, this fearful view of what is happening to the natural world comes at a strange time in the history of Britain. Today the birthplace of the Industrial Revolution is infinitely cleaner and greener than it was a century ago. The black soot which covered everything in and around the cities and the vast coal-mining regions has nearly all been washed away. Many early industrial buildings look as ruined and ancient as Pharaohs' tombs and are hidden in woodland that has grown around the abandoned brickwork. And despite two centuries of very rapid industrial change, something like eighty-five per cent of this small, and heavily populated, island is rural – all the roads and towns and power stations and chemical works together take up only about twelve per cent of the land.

A great deal of wildlife in Britain has been recovering from the worst assaults of industrialism in recent years and species that were close to extinction and confined to a few remote areas are expanding their range again. They are able to do so because the landscape of modern Britain remains remarkably hospitable to wildlife, and wild plants and animals have proved to be far more resilient to change than was once believed possible. This book, and the television series it accompanies, is about the way in which the forces of industrialism have changed the landscape of the first industrial nation and how it is that wildlife has survived so well. Very few species of bird, mammal, fish, insect or plant have become extinct in Britain in the past two centuries, and though quite a number have lost ground and are confined to a few areas, other species have thrived and are doing better now than they were in the eighteenth century.

It is at first surprising that industrialism has not been more destructive, for the world it has created appears to us so unnatural and synthetic that we can imagine very little wildlife tolerating it at all. In one very specific way this is true: not much in the way of plant or animal life could live in the blackest of the coal-mining areas when they were blanketed in smog and doused with acid rain. The cutting of canals, the laying of railway lines, the building of motorways and of huge towns all began as very destructive acts, wiping out fields and woodland and evicting the wildlife that was there. But, in time, the wounds begin to heal and some wild plants and animals have always returned and reclaimed the ground they lost.

OPPOSITE *A tawny owl among the monumental ruins of iron furnaces at Blists Hill, Ironbridge in Shropshire. These night-time hunters have done well in the past century, nesting in towns and areas of industrial decline*

Once you have an eye for it, you can see this process in action all over the country. Along the motorways, the verges are often resplendent with wild

The otter appeared to survive the onslaughts of early industrialism, but was in serious trouble in the 1950s, probably because of pesticide poisoning. It is now protected by law and is beginning to recover with the help of conservationists

flowers, and above the grass verges there are always small falcons hanging in the air, kestrels hunting for voles that colonize the broad embankments. In the temperate climate of north west Europe, trees grow easily and quickly and woodland returns with surprising speed to hide the evidence of mine workings and abandoned settlements. And with the trees come the woodland creatures: badgers, foxes, woodpeckers and butterflies.

It is only on ground badly poisoned by mining or industrial activity that the natural world is slow to reassert itself, but even the most desolate places are soon colonized by a few plants which are able to evolve rapidly enough to cope with the unusual soil conditions. One or two plants appear to have developed a kind of taste for polluted places which they help to detoxify. Norfolk Reed, the kind used in thatching pretty country cottages, is one of these and it is at the centre of some exciting research on the possibilities of ecological solutions to industrial pollution.

However, it is misleading to think of the effects of industrialism on the landscape as confined to factories and toxic waste, or mining or the building of great towns. The historical catchphrase 'Industrial Revolution' means much more than technological change, the replacement of water and horse power by steam engines and petrol-driven machines. Industrialism changed everything in Britain. The population rose dramatically and became concentrated in towns, leaving many rural areas less busy than they had been in the eighteenth century. The basis of wealth changed, and with that, the way in which the land was managed. And these broader changes, brought about by the forces unleashed by industrialism, have had a far greater impact on the wild plants and animals of the country than the rise and decline of mining or manufacturing.

The Victorians, as in their attitude towards sex, had a contradictory and in many ways hypocritical view of wildlife. On the one hand there was a great love of nature, expressed in the crazes for collecting plants and insects and the romantic treatises on the wonders of the natural world. On the other hand, even the most romantic of naturalists walked the countryside with a shotgun, potting at specimens, particularly rarities which had the greatest value as trophies.

Hunting and shooting took on a new social meaning and a new importance in the nineteenth century. In particular, the shooting of what was classified as game – partridge, pheasant, grouse, hares and rabbits – was made a special privilege of the well-to-do, and the right to shoot was turned into a way of establishing social status as the new wealth of industrialism merged with the old wealth of the landed aristocracy. As estates competed with each other for the favours of the aristocracy and Royalty by producing the biggest bag of birds during a season, anything which might get in the way of a successful shooting party was ruthlessly hunted down. The draconian game laws led to bloody battles between poachers and gamekeepers, and a great deal of wildlife was trapped and snared and poisoned if there was any suspicion it might take the eggs or young of pheasants. Badgers, hedgehogs, foxes, stoats, weasels, polecats, pine martens, kestrels, buzzards, sparrowhawks, falcons of all kinds, jays and magpies were all slaughtered on a staggering scale.

The great era of gamekeeping between the mid-nineteenth century and the First World War drove many of these species to near extinction and had a far greater impact on the fur and feather of British wildlife than any other episode in the history of industrialism.

At the same time, there was in the Victorian era the greatest enthusiasm for trying out new species in the British countryside. The native stock of wildlife

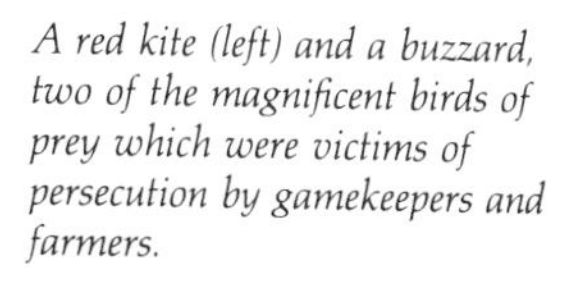

A red kite (left) and a buzzard, two of the magnificent birds of prey which were victims of persecution by gamekeepers and farmers.

appeared dull and limited compared with the exotic flora and fauna of the Empire, and there were many attempts to make hunting and shooting more interesting with the acclimatization of birds and animals from abroad. Most of these were unsuccessful. But some of the most interesting – though often problematic – wildlife around today is a legacy of that time – the grey squirrel, the red necked wallaby and the muntjac deer, for example.

Many native species were topped up with imports from Europe – roe deer from Germany and Siberia, red squirrels, badgers and foxes. It seems quite absurd that the Victorians should have imported foxes at a time when they were making such efforts to exterminate anything in the countryside which preyed on game birds. But the fox was given a very special status by the aristocracy and carefully

Badgers have withstood all the onslaughts of industrialism remarkably well. Despite badger baiting, persecution by farmers, and the constant upheavals of the landscape they have dug in and survived, sometimes reclaiming old industrial sites. It is estimated there are 250,000 adult badgers in Britain today.

nurtured in the countryside. Fox-hunting in its modern form had begun in the mid-eighteenth century and became important as a social ritual in the nineteenth century. Like shooting, fox-hunting was a feature of a newly industrialized nation in which the relationship between town and country and old and new wealth were changing. And there is little doubt that the fox greatly benefited, for though it was hunted up to six days a week during the season in some parts of the country, there was never any desire to get rid of it. On the contrary, it was nurtured like a sacred animal to be preserved for ritual slaughter.

Though fox-hunting and shooting still continue on a considerable scale, their impact on the wildlife of Britain is nothing like what it was a century ago. Foxes are so numerous now there is no need for any hunt to care for them in most parts of the country. Birds of prey that were so heavily persecuted are now protected, some of them carefully brought back to abundance by the Royal Society for the Protection of Birds. And many of the bizarre introductions of the Victorians, like the muntjac deer, are nibbling their way through the woodlands of Britain and eating rose bushes in suburban back gardens.

In the twentieth century, the greatest impact on wildlife has undoubtedly been brought about by the industrialization of agriculture. From the 1930s, the new pesticides and fertilizers produced by the chemical industry have made farming spectacularly successful. Powerful farm machinery has made it possible to remould the landscape more rapidly than ever before.

Most of this has happened since the Second World War, and it has been disastrous for some kinds of wildlife. In particular, the flowers of the fields – the familiar agricultural weeds – have disappeared from many areas. Sometimes this has been because of the use of herbicides, but more often because the soil has been made too fertile for them to thrive. The concentrations of nutrients in the soil have been washed into rivers and fed algae which consume all the oxygen and kill the fish. Persistent chemical toxins have also built up in the earth and from time to time produce a local ecological disaster. And in the 1950s and 1960s, DDT and other pesticides entered the food chain and began to kill birds of prey like the sparrowhawk and peregrine falcon which had begun to recover from the persecution by gamekeepers.

But this most recent assault on wildlife has come at a period quite late in the industrialization of the country, and some of its worst effects have been mitigated. For one thing, the desire to save wildlife from extinction has become a much more widespread and powerful force in our society. A new sensibility which began to take shape in the eighteenth century when the first effects of industrialism became apparent has culminated today in a degree of concern for the environment which would have been quite unimaginable two hundred years ago. This sensibility is one of the most important influences of industrialism and has become a worldwide force. It is a direct result of our mastery over nature which has transformed it from a threatening force into something delicate and in need of preservation.

The assault on the countryside by modern farming has reached its greatest intensity when some of the worst effects of industrialism are on the wane. Britain is littered now with regions of industrial dereliction – old coal mines, quarries, canals, disused railway lines and so on – which have become wildlife sanctuaries, cordoned off from the pressures of agriculture.

The process whereby the disappearance of natural habitats has been compensated for by the appearance of new, man-made sanctuaries has been going on since the start of industrialism. When the rivers were at their filthiest in the nineteenth century, new tracts of fresh water were provided by the canal system,

OVERLEAF *A profusion of poppies on newly dug soil. This is one weed species which thrives despite the over fertilisation of farmland which has made many wild flowers locally extinct.*

OPPOSITE *A male adder crossing the weird moonscape of an old china clay pit close to Corfe castle in Dorset. These snakes travel quite long distances in search of a mate, and the deserts of man-made dereliction sometimes provide them with essential habitat.*

abandoned when the railways arrived, and by the vast reservoirs created to provide drinking water for the towns. Today, wetlands destroyed by drainage for building or agriculture are replaced by flooded gravel pits dug to provide the material for building motorways and new towns. In central and southern England, there is now vastly more fresh water than there was two hundred years ago, allowing some species of waterfowl to thrive as never before.

Some of the most threatened habitats today are those which have lost their economic function in the countryside. They are indirect victims of industrial change. The great wastes of the heathlands, which provide snakes and lizards with the kind of open country they need in Britain, have been disappearing fast because they are no longer needed by country people for fuel or the grazing of animals. They would have disappeared much faster had there not been a demand for this kind of terrain for Army training, for golf courses, and on the moors for grouse shooting.

If all the most destructive effects of industrialism had occurred at the same time – the mining and burning of coal, gamekeeping, chemical and mechanized farming, the building of canals, railways and motorways – then the wildlife of Britain would have been very severely depleted. But the impact has been staggered. When industrial pollution was arguably at its very worst, farming was relatively primitive; when intensive agriculture began, much industrialism was in decline. For most species at most times, there has been somewhere to survive and from which to recover and to recolonize territory it had abandoned. And during the last century, its recovery has been greatly helped by the efforts of people who did not want it to disappear. The impulse to protect and preserve came just in time.

If this view of the effects of industrialism on our wildlife seems to be naïvely optimistic, it is worth considering how the record of the past two hundred years compares with that of early times. There is a tendency today to romanticize primitive economies and to see them as in harmony with nature. The hun-

RIGHT *Marbled white butterflies live on the chalk grasslands of southern England. The decline of sheep farming threatens their habitat – but the army training areas, such as Salisbury Plain, preserve some of the grasslands they need.*

OPPOSITE *Ducks and wading birds on migration still turn up in their thousands to feed on Seal Sands despite the heavy concentrations of chemical industries which have taken over the Tees estuary since the war. This remains an internationally important refuelling ground for migrant birds though 90 per cent of the mudflats have been reclaimed for industry.*

ter/gatherer takes the little that he needs to sustain himself, leaving the forest to close round again in a perpetually sustainable world rich in wildlife.

In Britain, and in most of Europe, the pre-industrial world was not like that at all. Using stone axes and fire, vast areas of woodland were destroyed to make way for pasture and arable land. All the most dramatic extinctions in Britain of the wolf, the bear, the wild boar, wild cattle were complete by the mid-eighteenth century. Inefficient agriculture requires enormous amounts of land and the woodland of Britain was scarce at the start of the Industrial Revolution. Much of it was preserved or planted for industrial use, for wood and charcoal were still essential for fuel in the eighteenth century as was timber for building ships and houses.

There is, in fact, more woodland in Britain today than there was two hundred years ago, a remarkable fact which flatly contradicts the impression most people have of what industrialism has done to this country. The fact that a large proportion of the new woodland is planted, non-native conifers – so disliked by conservationists – does not contradict this basic fact.

The chapters which follow attempt to substantiate what is currently a rather unfashionable view that the forces of industrialism are not necessarily at odds with the survival of wildlife, and that the natural world has a much greater resilience than this conservation-conscious age gives it credit for. Which is not to deny that the single most beneficial effect of industrialism has been to make people much more concerned about wildlife than at any previous period in history, and much more knowledgeable about how it behaves and how it might be preserved.

THI BRIDGE WAS CAST

1 Out of the Ashes

In tourist brochures, the small settlements of Coalbrookdale and Ironbridge in Shropshire bill themselves as the birthplace of the Industrial Revolution. Like all such claims this one is a little fanciful, for the transformation of the society and economy of Britain, and ultimately the world, did not begin at a specific time in any one place. And to visitors to the industrial museums here it must appear a very romantic notion that anything so powerful and devastating as industrialism could have its birthplace in this thickly-wooded gorge through which the River Severn runs, its banks overgrown and hung with trees. Twenty years ago, before industrial archaeologists began to excavate the ruins of the ironworks and mines here, it appeared that the Severn Gorge had hardly been touched by industrialism at all, for great trees had sprouted from the crumbling brickwork of the furnaces and had hidden them in woodland.

The rediscovery of the importance of this small region in the beautiful Shropshire countryside was like the unearthing of some ancient civilization. And yet Coalbrookdale and Ironbridge were the most industrialized place on earth only two centuries ago, and were not fully worked out and obsolete until late Victorian times. It is the speed at which the natural world has reclaimed these ruins which is at first so surprising, so exciting and thought-provoking. In recent years we have become accustomed to learning about the destruction wreaked on the natural world by the forces of industrialism, the loss of the last remaining piece of wild habitat, the endangering of species. We can hardly believe what we see at Ironbridge – the process in reverse, with the natural world growing again on the slag heaps of furnaces and prizing apart the brickwork with its roots.

In the woods that have sprouted from these industrial relics there is now a community of wild plants and animals which is colourfully representative of British natural history. There are polecats, badgers, rabbits, foxes, wild fallow deer, woodpeckers, kingfishers, kestrels, jackdaws, flycatchers, frogs, toads, newts, orchids – field-guides full of wildlife. And in order to reclaim this earth, once lost to the fires of industry, the plants and animals have not, for the most part, undergone any great evolutionary adaptations. They behave much as they have always done in the countryside.

Some creatures have made use of the ruins. A pair of kestrels nests in the shell of an old brickworks, a man-made cliff buried in woodland. Jackdaws raise their young in the stone walls of the tumbledown furnaces, and in the disused chimney pots. Deep in the woods, a community of badgers has adopted as the grand entrance to its sett – a maze of underground tunnels – a surviving brick arch about three feet high and four feet wide. Nearby, another sett has several small entrances with brick arches. It is an evocative sight which attracts groups of badger watchers who go there on summer evenings.

OPPOSITE *The world's first ever cast-iron bridge built in 1779 across the River Severn in Shropshire. Two centuries ago this was the most industrialised place on earth – in its ruination it has become rich in wildlife.*

Today, Ironbridge and Coalbrookdale are social and economic fossils set in attractive countryside. Their heyday was in the 18th century, at a time when industrialism was on a tiny scale. The incredible speed with which technology has grown since then is vividly illustrated by the view today of the gorge. From high on the ridge you can just make out the iron bridge itself, built in 1779 when it was a wonder of the world – the first ever bridge made from cast iron. Beyond, rising mountainously above the ridge of the gorge, are the cooling towers of the modern power station, belching clouds of steam into the sky. The iron bridge, spanning the Severn, is toy-like.

The first optimism that the sight of Ironbridge invokes – the overwhelming feeling that the natural world can heal the wounds of industrialism – gives way to the fear that what began here has now grown into such a monster it will, in the end, be devastating. Whereas trees and badgers could return to Ironbridge once it had gone into decline, the forces of modern industrialism may be too great now for them to cope with. All the warnings in recent years about the insidious effects of acid rain, and the climatic changes brought on by the greenhouse gases given off by power stations like that at Ironbridge suggest that what began here will, in the end, destroy the gorge.

And yet the descriptions of what Ironbridge was like in the late 18th century, and of the desolation of coal-based Victorian industry which followed it, is persuasive evidence that the natural world can, with a little time, re-inhabit places that were once quite hellish and devoid of any life other than that of the grimy miners, foundry workers and blinkered gin horses that kept its wheels turning. Historically, the recuperative power of nature has been perpetually reassuring. The dismal view of industrialism may yet be unnecessarily pessimistic.

The industrial museum at Blists Hill, the iron founding centre of the gorge, gives no idea today of what the place was like when Shropshire produced more iron than any county in England. There are charming recreations of candlemakers, workshops, Victorian bakers and chemists, a small foundry, a pub, a rustic settlement and a furry footed horse which clip-clops around with sacks of flour and bales of hay. The museum workers dress in period costume, and the whole effect is of a set for a Hollywood version of a Dickens novel. The past, it appears, must have been much more benign than the present.

But this is a far too quaint and pretty an impression of what the place was like: a point brought home amusingly by the lady in Victorian costume in the pie shop who pops the pasties into a microwave oven to heat them up. There is no smoke here, nor fearful noise, nor the dragon-fire of the furnaces which contemporary visitors to this place wrote about in the 18th century.

A great many tourists were attracted to Coalbrookdale at the time the Ironbridge was built 200 years ago because it represented such an extraordinary industrial scene. This is the description by an Italian visitor in 1787:

> *The approach to Coalbrookdale appeared to be a veritable descent to the infernal regions. A dense column of smoke rose from the earth; volumes of steam were ejected from fire engines; a blacker cloud issued from a tower in which was a forge; and smoke arose from a mountain of burning coals which burst into turbid flames. In the midst of this gloom I descended towards the Severn which runs slowly between two high mountains, and after leaving which passes under a bridge constructed entirely of iron. It appeared as a gate of mystery and, night already falling, added to the impressiveness of the scene, which could only be compared to the regions so powerfully described by Virgil.*

OPPOSITE *These derelict iron furnaces at Blists Hill in the Severn Gorge were lost in woodland and have been excavated as part of the Ironbridge Gorge museum. Jackdaws, starlings, wrens, kestrels, and many other birds nest in the ruined brick work.*

There were two things that made this narrow gorge remarkable. One was the intense concentration of all kinds of industry here – iron founding, limestone burning, brick and tile making. The other was the manufacture of very large cast iron structures, of which the Ironbridge itself was the great showpiece. The industrialization of the gorge was a result of the occurrence of coal, iron ore and limestone deposits next to the Severn river, which provided means for bulk

transport, and the tributary streams which provided power to drive mills and foundry hammers. Finally, its brief period of ascendancy in the early years of the 18th century was the result of an innovation in the smelting of iron which gave Shropshire an industrial lead.

In the early 18th century a Quaker ironmaster called Abraham Darby experimented with a new way of smelting iron, using coke instead of charcoal. It took him several years to perfect the system, but when he succeeded he transformed the business and made possible the manufacture of much larger amounts of iron and steel than ever before and the creation of the massive iron structures which now are so evocative of the great Victorian expansion of industry. Darby's iron smelters are the basis of the modern claim in the tourist brochures that this was the birthplace of the industrial revolution.

The great sources of power in medieval technology were wood, charcoal, horses and water. Water-powered mills ground corn, drove the hammers of iron forges, and were harnessed to an impressive array of wooden wheels which performed many other functions. Gin horses drove machinery too. The manufacture of iron cannon, swords, ploughs and other implements would involve all these sources of power. But charcoal was absolutely essential, for it was the only fuel pure enough to successfully melt down ironstone into pig iron which had the right properties for forging. Long before the 18th century, many other industries had converted to coal, which gradually became cheaper than either wood or charcoal. The Romans had coal mines in the north-east of England, and London was dependent on it for heating and for some of its industries by the late Middle Ages. It was brought in ships down the east coast from the Tyne coalfields and was known as sea-coal. By the 17th century, brewers and dyers had overcome their prejudice against coal, the dirtiness of which they thought would affect the quality of their produce. In 1553 the English trader William Cholmeley noted that the Flemish dyers did well with coal and he reported after a trip to Flanders:

> *I saye, that we have plentye of sea cole in many partes of this realme, so that we have them to serve our tune in dyinge as well as the Flemmings have . . . for they burne and occupye none other fuell than coles that are dygged out of the grounds, like as our smythes doe. Our dyeing therefore should not be wasteful to our wodis (woods) but rather a preserveyng. . .*

The conversion from wood and charcoal to coal was limited for most industries and for domestic use chiefly by the fact that it was found only in certain parts of the country. The winning of it was held back by primitive mining technology and its distribution was restricted by poor transport, along rivers, by sea or overland. Nevertheless, in the 17th century, the smiths of England used coal extensively for forging iron into pots and pans and nails, the last of which were in huge demand by the American colonies which were building great towns of wood hammered together with British nails. Coal had probably overtaken wood in importance as a national fuel by around 1600, and it was a worrying cause of pollution long before then. A Royal Proclamation of 1307 against the use of this fuel by the limeburners of London around Southwark, Wapping and East Smithfield, stated:

OPPOSITE *Industrial wastelands have often provided a haven for wildflowers driven from farmland by modern pesticides and fertilisers.*

> *As the King learns from the complaints of prelates and magnates of his realm, who frequently come to London for the benefit of the Commonwealth by his order . . . of his citizens and all his people dwelling there that the workmen now burn them and construct them of sea-coal instead of brush wood or charcoal, from the use of which*

> *sea-coal an intolerable smell diffuses itself throughout the neighbouring places and the air is greatly affected to the annoyance of the magnates, citizens and others there dwelling and to the injury of their bodily health.*

In the 18th century, Coalbrookdale – like most industrial parts of the country – used both coal and wood as fuel. Wood remained vital as the raw material for producing charcoal used in iron smelting. The charcoal burners used chiefly coppice wood, managed and cut on a system that had been in use right through the Middle Ages. A great variety of trees, including oak, hornbeam, beech and ash, were cut near the ground so that they would put up shoots which could be harvested on a cycle of 10 or 15 years and provide a constantly renewable source of fuel. To provide timbers for ships, building and machinery some trees were allowed to grow to maturity. A medieval wood, therefore, looked very different from those we see today. Much of it, the coppice, would be like an interminable thicket – until it was cut down, creating a clearing in the wood. It was valuable property, carefully managed, and the ironmasters would buy their coppice wood supplies well in advance.

There is some suggestion that when Abraham Darby came to Coalbrookdale from Bristol in the early 1700s he had difficulty getting coppice wood to fire the run-down iron smelter he had bought. The supply had been ordered years ahead by other ironmasters. This may have inspired him to experiment with other fuels, and to try coke. This is a purified form of coal, just as charcoal is purified wood. Not all coal will coke properly, a process which takes out many of the impurities. But Darby could get supplies from the Midlands and began to make pig iron using a coke-fired smelter around 1709. The reliance of a major industry on woodland for a critical fuel supply came to an end.

The consequences for the future of industry were immense. Darby's foundries made some of the early steam engines which ran on coal and provided the most important source of power until the invention of petrol engines and electricity generation.

The developments in the iron industry which Coalbrookdale set in train laid the foundations for the great expansion in the coal industry by improvements in mining technology, and ultimately in transport with the building of the railways. Woodland began to lose its economic value and the medieval system of management fell into disuse progressively all over the country. The iron smelting industry itself moved out of the woodland and on to the major coalfields, leaving Coalbrookdale behind. The heyday of the gorge was brief: even in the 1820s it was no longer a very remarkable place, as the centres of industry shifted to other regions. By the 1870s, the plants were returning, and saplings were sprouting from the ruins – the abandoned coppice wood around the gorge which had provided the fuel for Coalbrookdale's first industrial expansion had gone wild and was reclaiming the land.

As the Severn Gorge began to turn green again, the region to the east was turning black. The great manufacturing town of Birmingham was growing at a tremendous pace, and the Midlands industrial region was corroding the landscape on a scale which had been quite unimaginable in the 18th century.

From high above Britain, a speeded-up version of the spread of coal-mining in the 19th century would have appeared like the work of a giant mole, throwing up great heaps of black throughout the Midlands, Northumberland, Durham, Derbyshire, Nottinghamshire, South Wales and southern Scotland. As this dreadful creature worked its way along the richest seams, digging ever deeper as it followed the folds and faults of the subterranean rock, it spread soot across the land. And wherever coal was burned in any quantity, the air was thick with smoke and sparks so thick they sometimes set light to people in the blackened streets. Smoke billowed across the countryside as the railway network linked the great mole hills with the expanding cities.

This was the description of the Black Country, home of the iron founders of the Midlands, in 1851:

> *A perpetual twilight reigns during the day, and during the night fires on all sides light up the dark landscape with a fiery glow. The pleasant green of pastures is almost unknown; the streams, in which no fishes swim, are black and unwholesome; the natural dead flat is often broken by huge hills of cinders and spoil from the mines; the few trees are stunted and blasted; no birds are to be seen, except a few smoky sparrows, and for miles on miles a black waste spreads around where furnaces continually smoke, steam engines thud and hiss, and longchains clank, while blind gin-horses walk their doleful round.*

This was how the area between Manchester and Birmingham in 1835 was described:

> *About Wolverhampton, trees, grass and every trace of verdure disappear. As far as the eye can reach, all is black, with coal mines and ironworks, and from this gloomy desert rise countless slender pyramidical chimneys whose flames illumine earth, while their smoke darkens the heavens; the whole is exceedingly striking, probably unique of its kind.*

The terrible scale of industrial pollution in the Victorian era puts the story of little Coalbrookdale into perspective. Britain had much greater coal deposits than other European countries and it became a major exporter in the 19th century. The historic peak of mining was reached in 1914, by which time vast areas of the country had been poisoned, and once rural areas had been turned into what looked like volcanic wastes. The air in towns, and for miles around, was thick with smoke.

But if you fly over the Midlands or the north-east of England today, the towns are set in green countryside. You will see wooded hills, and the shimmer of lakes, many of which are overgrown pit heaps or sunken mine workings flooded with water. The natural world has healed the scars of Victorian industrialism with a rapidity and completeness just as startling as the greening of Coalbrookdale. What happened in the Severn Gorge has continued to happen as industrialism has evolved and, today, beneath the fields and woods of much of England are the tell-tale signs of a grimy and glorious industrial past.

It is not only abandoned iron works and coal mines that have become green again. In Cornwall there are the tin and copper mines, their ruined engine houses standing like old castles among the fields. River valleys lined with rotting mills which once ground the ingredients for gunpowder. Worked-out limestone quarries covered in orchids in the summer and filled with the song of willow warblers. Old clay pits which provide the arid conditions in which Britain's few varieties of snakes and lizards thrive. Abandoned quarries which have been colonized by bats so successfully that they are valued as sites of special scientific interest.

Just as Coalbrookdale began a very destructive process of industrialism, so its re-colonization by the natural world provides a model for reclamation by the natural world. This is not an archaic and isolated case of the return of the wild possible only at the dawning of industry – the powerful and brilliantly complex mechanisms of the natural world bide their time and begin to move in as soon as the wheels of industry grind to a halt and begin to rust. Look at the canals, once the industrial arteries of Britain, and the railways, now cherished in their ruination by conservationists all over the country as wonderful habitats for wildlife.

In its own way, the natural world is quite as dynamic as the industrial world, and the tendency to regard it as terribly precious, as a fixed and diminishing resource, is what has led many people to the quite false conclusion that the modern world must have been disastrous for wildlife. If somebody cuts down a wood to build a housing estate or a motorway, they imagine that the amount of woodland in Britain has been reduced for ever. They leave out of the equation the growth of trees where there were none before. When they look at a river, like the Severn in Shropshire, they worry about pollution from agriculture or acid rain, and forget that 200 years ago it was heaving with iron barges and shipping, and that its tributaries were lined with mills and iron foundries. As they stroll through woodland, abandoned and overgrown, they forget that it once resounded to the sounds of industry. So successful has the natural world been at covering the scars of past industrialism that we forget that it was ever there, and imagine that an overgrown pit heap is a precious piece of primeval woodland.

When an abandoned tin mine or iron furnace or coal tip returns to nature, it is the plants which arrive first. Without them very little insect or animal life can survive. The soils of dereliction are often poor in nutrients at first so that they are colonized by a group of plants which thrive on impoverished earth. A great many of the agricultural weed species favour poor soil, and cannot tolerate the artificial enrichment of modern farming. Orchids, which have a very complex ecology, often do very well in disused limestone quarries, and on the wastelands of industry. In Coalbrookdale they have colonized the old quarry which provided limestone for the ironworks – lime is used as a flux in the smelting down of iron ore. On a disused open cast coal mine, mosses normally only found on the thin soils of Snowdonia above 3,000 feet have taken root, to the delight of the local wildlife groups. More impressively, a variety of trees has sprouted from the lava-like dumps of iron foundry slack which line the bottom of the Severn Gorge several feet thick in places. There are birch and willow and oak. Into this burgeoning woodland have come the birds and the mammals. There are rabbits everywhere among the overgrown ruins, and hunting them there are now polecats, the wild ancestor of the ferret, which a century ago appeared to be doomed to extinction in Britain. The story of the revival of the polecat is not a simple one of a creature driven out of its former territory by the fires of industry only to return when the furnaces have fallen into ruin. As with all wildlife, the impact of human activity has been much more pervasive than that, and its revival was neither inevitable nor easily foreseen.

Contemporary accounts of the wildlife of Shropshire towards the end of the 19th century record a great decline in the number of polecats. This was general throughout Britain at a time when such predatory animals were ruthlessly persecuted.

Like much wildlife, polecats would have happily survived the destruction of former habitat by industrial expansion had they not been hunted down in the countryside. They were driven out of England not by the pollution of mines nor the heat of the iron furnaces but by gamekeepers who would not tolerate any wild animal which preyed on pheasant or partridge or any game that the privileged few shot for sport. Polecats were, in this sense, the victims of industrialism only indirectly, for the rise of modern game shooting arose from the social and economic forces released by industry (see Chapter Four).

Polecats are the wild ancestors of the domestic ferret, and have a particular taste for rabbit which they now hunt around the ruins of the old iron furnaces in the Severn Gorge.

By the beginning of the 20th century, the persecution of polecats had led to their extermination nearly everywhere in Britain except for the wildest parts of Wales. Here they hung on until the social and economic climate changed – gamekeeping declined and a modern sensibility which cherished all wildlife for its own sake took hold. Polecats slowly increased in numbers and they began to move back into England. Shropshire, on the Welsh border, was one of the first counties they re-colonized and the ruins of Coalbrookdale provided them with a new hunting ground. Polecats are now heading for the Midlands and, in time, might become common again throughout England.

Had polecats been driven to extinction in Britain, as they very nearly were, there would obviously have been no possibility of them re-colonizing the ruins of a place like Coalbrookdale, however green it had become. Unless, of course, these animals had been reintroduced from some other part of Europe. They survived largely by chance. But, having survived, they have made their own way back into the overgrown industrial landscape. And that has proved to be far more hospitable than might be imagined.

There is no logical or ecological reason why these animals should not reclaim a great deal of the territory they lost in the 19th century, for human sympathy is now with them much more in our industrialized world and there is plenty of habitat which is suitable for them.

The history of the badger is quite different from that of the polecat. There was no time when it was threatened with extinction, even though it has suffered cruelly over the centuries and is still persecuted today illegally by badger baiters and killed legally in areas where it is suspected of spreading tuberculosis to herds of cattle. In the 18th and 19th centuries, badger baiting was quite common and many were killed by farmers and gamekeepers. Badgers were probably scarcer in many areas then than they are today, though it is impossible to say what their numbers were at any one time for accurate records simply do not exist.

The return of badgers to the former industrial areas of the Ironbridge gorge is proof enough that they survived in the countryside around there right through the 18th and 19th centuries, for there is no suggestion that anybody deliberately reintroduced them. As the buildings of the gorge fell into ruin, and the trees grew back, badgers would simply reclaim lost ground. They eat worms and roots and small mammals so there is plenty of food for them here, and the woodlands of industrial dereliction tend to be quiet places in which badger colonies can live an undisturbed, nocturnal life. What they do need is soil in which they can dig their maze of burrows, and they have excavated these all over the steep sides of the gorge. One colony is established in an abandoned coal seam; another among the ruins of a brickworks.

It is all very reminiscent of the passage in *The Wind in the Willows* in which Mole is being shown around Badger's palatial subterranean home, and is deeply impressed by all the masonry, the pillars and arches and pavements.

> *'How on earth Badger,' he said at last, 'did you ever find time and strength to do all this? It's astonishing.'*
>
> *'It would be astonishing indeed,' said the Badger simply, 'if I had done it. But as a matter of fact I did none of it – only cleaned out the passages and chambers, as far as I had need of them. There's lots more of it, all round about. I see you don't understand, and I must explain it to you. Well, very long ago, on the spot where the Wild Wood waves now, before ever it had planted itself and grown up to what it now is, there was a city – a city of people, you know. Here where we are standing they lived, and walked and talked and slept and carried on their business. Here they stabled their horses and feasted, from here they rode out to fight or drove out to trade. They were powerful people, and rich and great builders. They built to last for they thought their city would last for ever.'*
>
> *'But what has become of them all?' asked the Mole.*
>
> *'Who can tell?' said the Badger. 'People come – they stay for a while, they flourish, they build – and they go. It is their way. But we remain. There were badgers here, I've been told, long before that same city ever came to be. And now there are badgers here again. We are an enduring lot, and we may move out for a time, but we wait, and are patient, and back we come. And so it will ever be.'*

Badger then explains to Mole how the animals return, how they have no care for history and simply move in to a place that suits them, and even if the place is a 'bit humpy and hillocky, and naturally full of holes', that was really only an advantage to a badger. He concludes by saying that the Wild Wood is 'pretty well populated by now; with all the usual lot, good, bad and indifferent – I name no names. It takes all sorts to make a world.'

The community of species which moves back into a place like the Ironbridge Gorge is not, however, representative of the beasts that lived in the wildwood before people arrived there. Not all the birds, plants and mammals have returned or can return. Wolves, bears and wild boar, for example, were gone before the dawning of industrialism, driven out of Britain by the destruction of the forests.

OPPOSITE *These badger cubs are rooting amongst the wild garlic that grows on the buried brick tunnels of an old brickworks.*

The native deer had disappeared too, both red deer and the smaller roe deer. In Ironbridge now the only wild deer are fallow, a species imported by the Normans from Europe. These have escaped from park herds. There have also been sightings of little muntjac deer, introduced to parks in Britain from India and China during the last century and now wild in much of the countryside. Badger has some strange companions in the wood now.

Unless it is deliberately reintroduced, a species has to have a place to hide, somewhere to survive from which it can recolonize an area. In a small island like Britain, extinction is final – wolves and bears cannot return from their last strongholds in central Europe because they cannot cross the sea from France. Large beasts like red and roe deer cannot easily move across such a heavily populated and cultivated country as Britain: they are cut off from places like Ironbridge even if it has become a favourable habitat for them once again.

It is no problem at all for birds to move about the country, because they can fly. Quite a few of the summer visitors to a place like Ironbridge – the swallows and martins that skim over the river, the flycatchers and the warblers – arrive each year from as far away as Africa. The only inhibiting thing for them is the food supply, and the availability of suitable nesting places. Some have disappeared from Ironbridge not because of industrialism but because their success has been affected some way or other elsewhere.

Until about twenty years ago, the Severn Gorge here was the northernmost nesting area for the nightingale, a summer migrant from Africa. It is probable that the nightingale was a visitor to the gorge right through the most industrial period for there would have been plenty of the habitat it likes most in which to nest – woody undergrowth. The coppice wood essential to provide charcoal for iron smelting is ideal for nightingales, whereas the overgrown, untended woods that have sprouted from the industrial ruins are not so good. Recently conservationists have begun coppicing to try to entice the nightingale back, but without success. It seems that the range of this little bird has shrunk southwards and that it does not take up nest sites in many areas even though they are available. There is plenty of insect food for it, probably as much as there has ever been, so it is not a lack of food or habitat that has reduced its numbers but some other factor in its complex life.

Though the nightingale is no longer there, it is heartening that all three species of woodpecker now nest in the gorge. Most of the trees are not more than a century old, and many much younger, yet woodpeckers can survive here. They do so in different ways, for the behaviour of these apparently similar birds is much less alike than one might imagine.

The green woodpecker, the largest of the three, does not produce the drumming sound of the cartoon Woody Woodpecker. It has a kind of mocking call, like shrill laughter, and is known as a "yaffle" in some places because of this. Often the green woodpecker is a parkland rather than a woodland bird because its favourite food is ants, and these are found in greatest abundance on grazed grassland. The green woodpecker's ideal habitat is a place like Richmond Park in London which has old oak trees, which provide plenty of nesting holes and plenty of hummocky, ant-hill grassland. Nevertheless, it is there in the gorge yaffling away in summer, and putting together the elements that it needs to survive where the regenerated woodland of the gorge meets the pastures of the plateau above.

Whereas the green woodpecker is quite a large and conspicuous bird, a bright green with a flash of red on its head, the lesser spotted woodpecker is hardly ever seen at all. It is tiny, only the size of a sparrow, much too small, you would

OPPOSITE *The tragedy of dutch elm disease which altered the landscape of much of Britain was at least good news for the great spotted woodpeckers which found abundant food in the dead trees.*

think, for a bird which hammers holes in trees. But this little woodpecker does bore out nesting holes in the wood of rotten branches, and it does drum in the classic fashion. Many people have the idea that the woodpecker uses its ability to hammer at wood with its specially designed shock-absorbing beak and head in order to dig out insect food. In fact the sound is purely for display – it is part of its ritual for establishing a territory. The noise it manages to make is quite extraordinary, the resonance of the tree amplifying the sound which travels through woodland with great penetration.

The lesser spotted woodpecker is there in Ironbridge Gorge, drumming away in March. And so too is its larger namesake, the great spotted woodpecker. It is a startling bird to see in the English landscape, pied like a panda, and the male with a splash of red on the back of its head. It is a bit smaller than the green woodpecker, but much larger than the lesser spotted woodpecker which it resembles in colouring. And it is much more truly a woodland bird, though it has been very successful in the new savannah of mature suburbia, where it will join other birds feeding on peanuts in the winter. The drumming of the great spotted woodpecker, eight to ten blows on a tree branch or sometimes a telegraph pole delivered in a single second, is again a territorial signal and the most familiar woodpecker sound in the countryside. It is heard mostly in early spring when the birds are taking up nesting sites and seeking mates.

A young great spotted woodpecker, one of the most colourful and successful of birds in twentieth-century Britain. Its numbers have increased steadily, and with it the characteristic drumming sound of the woodpecker hammered out on a resonant tree branch.

The fact that these three woodpeckers are in the Ironbridge Gorge is proof enough that the re-established natural world is sufficiently rich to support a range of species with quite exacting and rather different lifestyles. But the new wildwood here has some notable absentees. Though there are no native deer here it is possible that, in the next few years, some might arrive as they expand their range within England. Roe deer are not far away and though they are a species which tends to stick close to a home territory, their numbers and range appear to be growing steadily.

Though roe are now one of the most numerous deer wild in Britain, few people think of them as a native British species the way they do of red deer. If you catch a glimpse of a deer darting away in woodland anywhere in the Midlands or southern England it is probably a roe. The roebuck has small, pointed horns and is quite a dangerous beast – it will attack people if it is cornered. But unless you go looking for roe you are unlikely to see them. The best time is in winter when they will leave the woods to graze on the new shoots of wheat. They will look up with the characteristic haughty alertness all deer seem to have, then turn to run with a flash of brown and bobbing white rump if you try to approach them.

There is a good reason there is so little popular awareness of the presence of roe deer in the woods: in 1800 they were, by all accounts, extinct in England. Much more familiar were the imported fallow deer which graced the surviving parks. In the days when stag hunting was the sport of kings, the native roe was not prized as a quarry as were the red deer stag and the fallow buck or hart. This was most likely because the roe is not a herd animal and is not easily kept and controlled in parks, as were the red and fallow deer that were hunted and prized for their venison which provided fresh meat in winter. The low status of roe deer appears to have left them at the mercy of a rural population that wiped them out. They were regarded as keepers' perks – meat that could legitimately be taken. The destruction of woodland with the spread of agriculture from Roman times left the roe few hiding places, and as it was not artificially maintained like roe and fallow deer, it became scarce even in the late Middle Ages. By 1800 the only surviving roe were in the lowlands of Scotland. It was probably extinct in the Ironbridge Gorge before the coke-fired furnaces began to make pig iron, so that it was not a victim so much of industrialism as of the spread of agriculture.

The return of roe deer to England was not a natural process, though their subsequent success has been. There are so many now in some parts of the country they are a problem for foresters because of the damage they do to trees, and they are culled. Roe deer were brought back to England. In the early 1800s, Lord Dorchester shipped roe down from Perthshire to his Dorset estate at Milton Abbas, and attempted to hunt them with stag hounds. In 1884, six pairs of roe deer from Württemburg in Germany were released in Suffolk, and the Duke of Bedford brought in some from Siberia to his Woburn estate. The roe around now are all descended from these introductions, and they are a hybrid lot, with a range of coat colours. But they are truly wild deer, and they have done well principally because of the planting of conifer woods during this century, and the regeneration of broad-leaved woods in many parts of the country.

Roe deer are now living wild in the woods that have been planted, or have seeded themselves on the abandoned pit heaps and mining settlements of the north-east of England. One such place is the lost village of Houghall just south of Durham city. The fact that a species of deer once extinct now haunts abandoned coal mines at Houghall is one of the most poignant truths about the brave new wilderness of Britain.

A mine was sunk in the 1840s, and quickly worked out, but the pit heap

ABOVE *A fallow stag, or hart. In some parts of the country these are the only wild deer. They are not native to Britain and were probably introduced by the Normans for food and for sport. Wild fallow have escaped from park herds.*

OPPOSITE *A roebuck among young pines: a poignant symbol of wildlife recovery in the past 200 years. Extinct in England in 1800 because of the destruction of woodland and persecution, roe deer were reintroduced by the Victorians and thrive in young woodlands in many parts of the country.*

survived until the 1930s, and a row of miners' terraced cottages, remained until the 1950s. You would never guess today that this patch of England was blanketed with smoke and resounded to the clanking of the pit wheel and the rattle of trucks a century ago, nor that people lived here only 30-odd years ago. The heap and part of the site were planted with conifers as part of an early reclamation scheme in the 1930s, but a range of trees has taken root there now and it blends in with the surrounding countryside.

In the wood that has grown on what was Houghall Heap there are a few relics of the mining era, and these have now been marked out as points to look for in a woodland walk – the old air shaft, safely covered with an iron grille, the green lane where the railway used to run, a map of where the streets were. The wood is thinnest where the last terraces remained and there are still doorsteps here, covered in green moss. By itself, the wood that was Houghall is not large enough to sustain an animal the size of a roe deer. But there has been enough reclamation now in the region as a whole for the overgrown ruins of the Durham mines to support roe and many other creatures. In fact, there may well be more roe deer here than at any time since the early Middle Ages.

If you add together all the Houghall Heaps in the country, all the places where woods have grown again, and leave aside the conifer plantations that have covered such large areas during this century, there is almost certainly more woodland in Britain now than 200 years ago. And in that woodland there is a greater variety and abundance of deer. For, alongside the roe, there are – according to region – wild fallow deer escaped from parks, muntjac deer from China and India, Chinese water deer and sika deer from Japan. Much more is said about these introductions in Chapter Four. The point to be made here is that since Britain became an industrialized nation from the mid-18th century, a long term trend in the decline of woodland and beasts of the forests has been reversed.

This is such a startling proposition, which runs contrary to everything that is said in the name of conservation about the destructiveness of industrialism, that it needs a bit of spelling out.

There is a popular idea of what has happened to the woods of this country which is encouraged by well meaning conservationist campaigns to save trees. It is, crudely speaking, that the island was once covered in extensive forests which have been whittled away over the centuries, first rather slowly, and then much more rapidly as towns were built and motorways laid across the land. A wood, once it has grown reasonably tall, appears to us to be a timeless, ancient place – a survival from a greener, less industrial past. But this view of our woodland – and that of much of North America and Europe for that matter – is seriously misleading. It is, in fact, wrong.

Britain was once entirely wooded, except for the highest mountain tops and the most windswept coasts. But that was at least 5,000 years ago. By Roman times it was not very wooded at all. Over several thousand years, people with stone axes, then bronze and iron axes and with fire had cleared the woods to get rid of fearsome beasts and to provide land for growing crops and to graze animals. By the Middle Ages, the surviving woodland was a valuable resource, as we have seen, and carefully managed. The demands of building and of industry, which required supplies of timber and firewood, led to the planting and preservation of trees. An estimate of woodland cover in England from the records of the Domesday Book in the 11th century is 20 per cent.

There were many scares in the 16th century that Britain would run out of wood – rather like the oil crises of today. But it has been shown conclusively by historical research that industry did not eat up woodland, in that it clear-felled an area and then moved on to the next bit. Farmers did that, and still do. But industrialists, for the most part, had to look after their fuel supplies, and the coppicing system, with varying degrees of efficiency, ensured that. The early substitution of coal began to relieve the pressure on woodland several centuries ago. An analysis of country maps puts woodland cover in the mid 18th century at around 6–7 per cent.

While woodland had an economic value it was relatively safe and the demands of industry for fuel and building materials was in effect a counter pressure to the demands of farmers for land. Some of the most wooded parts of the country today are those which were important industrial areas in the age of charcoal. This is true for the hills of the Weald south of London which, in the 16th century, resounded to the hammers of forges turning out armaments. As late as the 1720s, when this region was on the wane industrially, the writer Daniel Defoe noted on his journey between Guildford and Godstone a district:

> *Exceedingly grown with timber, has abundance of waste and wild grounds, and forests and woods, with many large iron works at which they cast great quantities of iron cauldrons, chimney backs, furnaces, retorts, boiling pots and all such necessary things of iron; besides iron cannon, bomb-shells, stink pots, hand grenades and cannon balls etc. in infinite quantity.*

OPPOSITE *Mistletoe, common in southern England and the midlands, is a parasitic plant almost exclusively found on deciduous trees. The plant is spread by birds which eat the berries and wipe the sticky seeds off their beaks on to the branches where they take root. The berries can be poisonous to humans.*

And what about the building of the British Navy? Surely that accounted for the felling of countless oak trees and the denuding of the landscape of its primeval forest? This is such a popular myth that it is still repeated whenever anyone takes a backward glance at British trees, as they did in October 1987 when hurricane force winds blew down great chunks of woodland in south east England. More destructive than the British Navy was the historical message.

The building of ships did consume a great deal of oak and other kinds of timber, and there were regular crises in supply. This was, for the most part, not for lack of oak trees, but timber of the right quality, shape and age, a scarcity brought on largely by the inefficiency and corruption of the authorities.

Many oakwoods were planted, or encouraged to spread naturally as a timber reserve, and because the bark of oak was essential for the tanning of leather, which was as important as plastic is today, when everything was horsedrawn and saddlery was a thriving trade. Many surviving oakwoods began not as preserved wildwood but as plantations created to sustain early forms of industry.

The most famous woodland for the supply of timber for the Navy was the Forest of Dean in Gloucestershire, which since Roman times had been an iron-producing region as well. Next in importance was the New Forest, though the quality of oak here was poorer because of the soil. Much of the New Forest had been planted by William the Conqueror to create a new hunting reserve, and to do so he had destroyed at least twenty villages and made up to 2,000 countryfolk homeless. In southern England oak was not even the dominant native tree – the latest scientific research suggests it was the now relatively scarce small-leaved lime (see Chapter Six).

In short, woodland in Britain has gone and come back, and has come back and gone again. It has never simply been a finite supply of trees which has been progressively whittled away. And it continues to return, with remarkable swiftness on any land of reasonable quality which is left unbuilt on, is not farmed and is not grazed by animals. It is a strange ecological twist of fate that the destruction of rabbits with the introduction of myxomatosis in 1953 greatly speeded the return of scrub and then woodland in many places because there were no animals left to graze the ground.

With the widespread distribution of coal by railway from the mid-19th century, the management of woodland by the coppicing or pollarding of trees stopped quite abruptly. You can see this quite clearly today in many places, and it is splendidly illustrated in some of the beech woods of the Chiltern Hills north of London. Until about the 1840s, when the coal-carrying trains arrived, the trees were cut regularly at a height which prevented browsing animals from eating the new shoots – they were pollarded to provide a renewable supply of firewood. Once the coal came in, they were left and the shoots have grown over more than a century into a great crown of heavy branches, many of which are now snapped. The trees are nearing the end of their natural life, which had been extended by constant pruning. As the beeches die off, other varieties of trees are moving in when the light penetrates the forest floor allowing saplings to grow. A wood is not static – it is dynamic. The lowest ebb for woodland cover, about 4 per cent, was in 1900. Today it is around 10 per cent, 60 per cent of which is conifer, and 40 per cent broad leaved.

Industrialism is certainly not responsible for the destruction of British woodland, any more than it is a uniquely damaging form of society for most forms of wildlife. It can be quite devastating, but so too were the activities of much more technologically primitive cultures which needed vast amounts of land to sustain very unproductive farming, and chopped down the wildwood of Britain

OPPOSITE *The long eared owl shares the same kind of territory as the tawny owl, but it has not done well this century. It is smaller than the tawny – which will kill and eat it. But exactly why the long eared owl has been declining nobody knows – it still thrives in Ireland where there are no tawny owls*

in order to feed themselves. There is a contemporary romanticism about earlier societies living in harmony with nature. In fact, they were engaged in a constant war with nature and it was on winning that war that their survival depended.

It is a prejudice, rather than a new understanding of the natural world, that makes for surprise that there is more woodland now than 200 years ago, or that there is a greater variety and quantity of deer in those woods. What most often has to be explained is not the survival of species since industrialism, but their success.

A rough tally of what has happened in the past two centuries to mammals, birds, fish, flowers, trees, insects, reptiles and other creatures does not show a universal decline. On the contrary, there is a greater variety of mammals now than then, and in some notable instances a greater quantity. None has become extinct. A number of introductions, such as the grey squirrel or muntjac deer, have become well established in the wild. Foxes are almost certainly more numerous, and it is possible badgers are too. Otters, on the other hand, appear to have declined. Deer have increased; pine martens and wild cats were driven to near extinction and are only just recovering their numbers.

It is the same contradictory story with birds. There is as great a variety of breeding birds now as 200 years ago, because the losses have been equalled by the gains. The barn owl and the long-eared owl have declined drastically, but the tawny owl has done much better. There are no hard and fast rules, nothing which supports the standard conservationist contention that industrialism is a universally destructive force.

The sparrowhawk was a victim first of the Victorian gamekeeper and later of pesticides, but it has now begun to revive in many parts of the country. Unlike the kestrel, it does not do well in towns; its method of hunting is not suited to built-up areas.

In many instances the threat to wildlife is not due to a direct assault by industrial development but to a decline in a pattern of life in modern society which undermines the maintenance of a particular kind of landscape. This is true of the shrinking of heathlands and grasslands – they have no economic value any more. Where they are sustained, it might be for reasons which have nothing to do with conservation as such (see Chapter Three). In the British climate, reptiles depend to a large extent on poor, arid soils which historically were the creation of human activity in the felling of trees. They thrive on areas affected by soil erosion.

In the south-west of England, a disused China clay pit or abandoned tin working will become a haven – a barren piece of ground in which the adder and the smooth snake, the common lizard and the sand lizard thrive. Worked-out limestone quarries harbour rare orchids. And so on.

When Victorian industrialism was at its most filthy and polluting, the farming land around was relatively benign. As industrial regions one by one went into decline, there was a rich source of recolonization in the fields around so that flowers and insects and birds would move back in to reclaim the land they had lost. Since the last war the regions of industrial dereliction have become quite vast, while the countryside has, in areas of intensive farming, become much less hospitable to much wildlife. The overgrown ruins of former industries have in this way become oases for wildlife, places from which the countryside might once again be colonized if the sprays and poisons are reduced and the land is less heavily fertilized. In some instances the value of industrial dereliction is well established – abandoned quarries are vital roosting places for many species of bat.

To survive, wildlife has to keep on the move, it has to be able to leave one region and take up residence in another. Many plants and birds and insects have very effective means of dispersal. Other species do not, and their survival – as in the case of roe deer – has been dependent on a conscious human effort to ship them around the country. In the case of frog and fish, there is hardly any need for them to have natural means of dispersal because so many are carried around from one pond or lake to another by schoolchildren or anglers.

This might seem very unnatural. But it is not. Hitching a ride from one place to another is a well established evolutionary practice, and for most wild creatures, how they travel is much less important than what they find when they get there. And within the landscape of modern Britain, there is a rich variety of habitats in which wildlife can live.

In some instances, that habitat has actually been increased, quite inadvertently, by some of the human activities which are regarded by most people as terribly destructive – the building of motorways and concrete office blocks. It is to this that we turn in the next chapter.

2 Mink and Cement Mixers

Close to the first section of motorway ever built in this country, the southerly end of the M1, is a wonderful nature reserve, a series of lakes fringed with reeds and willow and dotted with wild duck. At sunset the skeins of geese which fly in paint a picture of primeval natural beauty. This is Great Linford, where the Game Conservancy has a research station. After dark, a small bright-eyed predator goes in search of prey – fish, small mammals, duck and other water birds. Its prey is abundant and will include from time to time the chicks of one of the most beautiful and fascinating of birds, the great crested grebe. Not far away, traffic flows along the motorway, the streams of car headlights winding through the dark like molten iron in the blackness of a furnace.

In the morning, research workers at Great Linford will find the remains of a grebe and curse the mink. It is a small drama enacted many times as ecologists struggle to create a balance in a natural world which has developed a life of its own in an environmental and historical setting which has been created entirely by human activity, and mostly by accident.

The nature reserve is owned by the Amey Roadstone Company, sand and gravel extractors, who supplied much of the hardcore and cement for the building of the M1 back in the 1960s. Most deposits of these materials essential to the concrete world were laid down in river valleys, and when the extraction is complete, they are liable to flood. Great Linford, which looks so natural, is a set of flooded gravel pits. The North American mink has been moving across Britain since it escaped from fur farms in the 1950s. It was first found to be breeding in the wild in Devon. It is now established at Great Linford, a legacy of the fashion for fur coats.

In the late 19th century, the great crested grebe was hunted to near extinction in Britain to satisfy an earlier fashionable demand. Its wings were used as 'grebe furs' to adorn the shoulders of dresses worn by society ladies in the late Victorian period, when plumage was all the rage. It was saved by a combination of a change in fashion, the rise of a bird protection movement, and a great increase in its habitat. The reedy waters of the shallower gravel pits are tailor-made for the grebe which builds its nest next to the shore and feeds almost entirely on fish, for which it dives. Great crested grebes are now so successful they are breeding quite wild on the Serpentine in Hyde Park and they can be seen wintering on the Thames right in the centre of London.

Everyone applauds the success of the grebe; the reception for the alien mink is much less warm. In the daemonology of rural/industrial England, it has replaced the fox as the most hated predator. You will hear it described by otherwise unemotional people as a 'ruthless killer'. That is, of course, how it survives and waterfowl make up a large part of its diet. The mink can swim and climb and move with lightning speed. It has a much smaller territory, and a very different pattern of behaviour, from the otter. But it is now a well established part of British wildlife, listed in all the field guides to mammals. And it is, in logic, as British as the rabbit, the grey squirrel or fallow deer, all alien introduced species.

OPPOSITE *A kestrel hunting by a motorway where the grass verges, out of bounds to the public, have become a wildlife haven. Though motorways have destroyed a good deal of countryside the digging of sand and gravel to build them has created a new lakeland in central and southern England.*

It is nevertheless true that the community of plants, animals and insects which colonizes a recently worked-out and flooded gravel pit is likely to be bizarre and subject to very rapid change in the first few years. In time, a stable semi-natural ecosystem might arise but it would not be the same as a freshwater lake which had been in the same area for many thousands of years.

But where are these natural lakes with which we might compare the flooded gravel pit? The answer, for most of the Midlands and a very large part of southern England, is that there are none. Lakes are formed naturally only under certain conditions. There are oxbow lakes in the valleys of meandering rivers, lagoons left as the watercourse changes in time. There are the glacial lakes of Cumbria and the Scottish Highlands, formed in the hollows scooped out in the last Ice Age. There are meres on very boggy, peaty soils. But natural freshwater is relatively scarce except, of course, in rivers.

It is a remarkable truth that the activities of builders of canals, brickworks, motorways, new towns, office blocks and many other industrial structures have vastly increased the amount of freshwater in Britain. In addition, there are the reservoirs which provide drinking water or were formed to maintain the waterflow in canals or were created to provide a run-off for mills driving forge hammers and the wheels of industry in an earlier era. Since the mid-19th century, many ponds in villages and on farmland have disappeared with the decline of horse-power and the drove roads of cattlemen. These watering holes later fell into disuse and became dry land again as the trees were allowed to grow around them and fill them with leaves. A natural process has, therefore, removed a lot of freshwater, while industrialism has created a great deal more.

The North American mink, brought in by fur farmers in the inter-war years, has gone wild and spread throughout the country since the 1950s. It is much more successful than the otter, and is a great exploiter of gravel pit lakes.

The single most dramatic increase in lakes since the Second World War has been brought about by the creation of flooded gravel pits which is a direct consequence of a massive increase in the demand for sand and gravel. When a gravel pit is worked out, it can be filled with solid material – rubbish of some kind as a rule – covered with earth and turned back into agricultural land. However, the rising demand for lakes for all kinds of watersports has led to many more pits being flooded since the last war.

Here are some statistics. People have been digging holes in the ground for thousands of years to provide lime, clay, marl and so on, essential raw materials for industry and farming. But during this century the demand for sand and gravel has risen far above anything known in the past. Around 1925, about five million tonnes of sand and gravel were dug up each year. By 1940 this was 30 million tonnes. Demand increased sharply after the last war and reached a peak of 110 million tonnes in 1972 at the height of the motorway building programme. It has fallen back now to around 90 million tonnes but is maintained at a high level chiefly by private house building. A large part of the sand and gravel taken from Great Linford went into the construction of Milton Keynes.

The proportion of gravel pits which are flooded when worked out has also risen since the 1940s: in 1970 it was around 63 per cent. Nearly all these pits are concentrated in central and southern England for two reasons. Firstly, sand and gravel are found in the alluvial plains of large rivers: the Thames, the Trent and the Ouse. Secondly, it is in these prosperous parts of the country where the demand for materials has been greatest. An entirely new lakeland has been created and, in these regions, has had a tremendous influence on wildlife – particularly, as you might expect, the duck population. Those who like to shoot duck, the wildfowlers, have taken a greater interest in the development and ecology of gravel pits than any other group.

When a gravel pit is newly flooded, it is likely to be a barren place with unsightly muddy banks and very little vegetation. Birds can find it and colonize it quickly enough for they can fly and have no trouble reaching new territories. But freshwater is not much use to them until it has matured and developed some kind of community of plants, insects, crustacea and fish.

A thorough study of how the ecosystem of a brand new gravel pit develops has yet to be done, but it is possible to say what the principles are and what is likely to happen. It is a wonderfully intricate subject, for the way in which plants and animals disperse and the stages of what is called 'ecological succession' – the timetable of arrival and competition between species – takes into account many thousands of delicate mechanisms.

It is a problem that fascinated Charles Darwin when he was developing the theory of evolution in *The Origin of Species*. He had observed that the same, or very similar, freshwater species of fish, mollusc and plant occurred in rivers and lakes which were completely isolated from each other by land. Their widespread distribution on a continent could not be explained by their movement through water so they must have some other means of dispersal.

In the case of fish, it seemed unlikely that they could travel through air except in the case of whirlwinds in India which could suck them out of one river and deposit them in another. The likely explanation for the occurrence of the same species in isolated rivers or lakes was that the water level was once much higher and the fish evolved when the waterways were connected. They had subsequently become isolated. You can explain in this way the descendants of migratory fish in entirely landlocked European lakes: they got there during the early stages of glacial retreat when rivers linked the lakes with the sea.

In the case of gravel pits, flooding appears to be the only means whereby fish from rivers can naturally colonize new lakes. As most pits are in the flood plains of rivers which laid down the sand and gravel in the first place, this is a perfectly feasible explanation.

In a country with an estimated three million anglers, it is also more than likely that the first fish into a newly flooded gravel pit arrive in the back of a car and are tipped in in bucket loads, in much the same way as schoolchildren effectively redistribute frogs by collecting them in one spot and releasing them in another.

Stories about fish eggs being carried on ducks' feet appear to be fanciful: nobody has ever given scientific proof that it can happen. But a great deal of use to fish and fowl can be transported in this way. Charles Darwin himself conducted some interesting experiments to see how this might be done. In *The Origin of Species* he wrote:

> *I could not understand how some naturalized species have rapidly spread throughout the same country. But two facts, which I have observed – and no doubt many others remain to be observed – throw some light on this subject. When a duck suddenly emerges from a pond covered with duck-weed, I have twice seen these little plants adhering to its back; and it has happened to me, in removing a little duck-weed from one aquarium to another, that I have quite unintentionally stocked the one with freshwater shells from the other. But another agency is perhaps more effectual: I suspended a duck's feet which might represent those of a bird sleeping in a natural pond, in an aquarium, where many ova of fresh-water shells were hatching: and I found that numbers of the extremely minute and just hatched shells crawled on the feet and clung to them so firmly that when taken out of the water they could not be jarred off, though at a somewhat more advanced age they would voluntarily drop off. These just hatched molluscs, though aquatic in nature, survived on the duck's feet, in damp air, from twelve to twenty hours: and in this length of time a duck or a heron might fly at least six or seven hundred miles ...*

The calculations are characteristic of Darwin's meticulousness as a researcher, as was his further experimentation with pond mud.

> *I do not believe that botanists are aware how charged the mud of ponds is with seeds; I have tried several little experiments, but will here give only the most striking case: I took in February three tablespoonfuls of mud from three different points, beneath water, on the edge of a little pond: this much when dry weighed only six and three quarter ounces; I kept it covered up in my study for six months, pulling up and counting each plant as it grew; the plants were of many kinds, and were altogether 537 in number; and yet the viscid mud was all contained in a breakfast cup! Considering these facts, I think it would be an inexplicable circumstance if water birds did not transport the seeds of fresh-water plants to vast distances ...*

In this way, water birds – ducks, herons, grebe, moorhen, coots – will begin the process of creating a well-stocked pond which, in time, might provide them with food and a place to nest. Because most gravel pits are dug not far from rivers, and are usually excavated next to a worked-out pit that is already becoming overgrown, the process of colonization can begin quite rapidly. But dispersal remains haphazard and no two gravel pits will develop in the same way: their geology, depth, position and so on will all affect the kind of habitat they become. It is the shallower lakes which are the most productive and nowadays a gravel pit which is to become a nature reserve is generally sculpted with a bulldozer to provide wide gently-sloping banks in which plants can take root.

In the first few years of the development of a new lake there is a shortage of

At the turn of the century the great crested grebe was close to extinction in Britain: it is thought only 42 pairs survived when legal protection saved it from the trade in feathered hats and dresses. Gravel pit lakes provided the grebe with new habitat and it is now very successful, with an estimated 6,000 breeding pairs in Britain.

food and great competition for it, the most fierce rivalry taking place between fish and ducks searching for the same insects, grubs and molluscs. At Great Linford they have found that they can increase the wildfowl population by keeping the fish numbers down. The fortunes of different kinds of duck wax and wane according to the kind of food available. Diving ducks, like tufted, need a good supply of freshwater shellfish, like water snails.

Since the 1960s, tufted duck have done extremely well in Britain and the numbers of breeding pairs is estimated to have increased about four times. The great increase in the number of flooded gravel pits is thought to be largely responsible. The great crested grebe is also very common and a recent estimate was that half the population was on man-made lakes of one kind or another.

Industrialism has, in fact, had an enormous impact on freshwater in Britain from its very earliest days. It has been harmful in many ways but the overall effect has been to increase the numbers and range of many species. This is particularly so with fish. There have been a couple of extinctions (the burbot for example) of fish which occurred only locally, a great reduction in the migratory fish of many rivers, particularly salmon, a great redistribution and probably an increase in common fish such as the roach, and the introduction of twenty new species, with variable results. The worst period for fish was probably from the mid-19th century until the 1950s when the pollution of rivers with sewage and industrial waste killed off many of them entirely, or over a great part of their course. Fish have now come back either through natural colonization from unpolluted tributaries or from restocking.

OVERLEAF *Great Linford gravel pits, dug to build the M1 motorway and the new town of Milton Keynes, are now a superb nature reserve and the headquarters of a Game Conservancy research station.*

How well fish fared in the early days of industrialism nobody knows, for the records are scanty. But the flora and fauna of rivers and streams must have been greatly altered during the Middle Ages for water power was vital for industry and the larger rivers provided the main transport routes for bulk goods when roads were unmetalled and often unusable for much of the year. Freshwater fish were an important food inland when sea fish could not be transported far and when the religion of the nation required adherence to dietary rules: fish on Friday. There were fish ponds in the grounds of monasteries and large houses and many conflicts between those who wanted fish from the river and those who wanted to harness its power or use it for navigation.

The Domesday inspectors recorded 5,624 water mills in England at the end of the 11th century. On some rivers they were closely packed: the Wylye in Wiltshire had 30 mills on a ten-mile stretch. Mills were important not only for grinding corn, but for fulling – beating – cloth, forging iron, pulping paper and working the bellows of blast furnaces. Most mills were on the smaller faster–flowing streams and the flow of water was controlled with ponds and channels. There were many conflicts between one mill owner and another, and between those trying to haul goods up a stream and those regulating the flow. The bargees were obliged to bargain with mill owners for a 'flash' – a run of water – to get up some stretches.

From 1600 great efforts were made to increase the navigable range of the main rivers. In the 17th century there were about 685 miles of navigable waterway in England, the chief rivers being the Severn, the Trent, the Great Ouse and the Thames. With dredging and pound locks, this had been increased to 1,160 miles by the middle of the 18th century. Tributaries of the major rivers, such as the Kennet running into the Thames, were opened up to water traffic and entirely new rivers were made navigable, such as the Hampshire Avon between Salisbury and the coast.

But the eastern waterways were completely isolated from those in the west and one of the great projects of the age of canal building was to link these to create a nationwide transport network. The brief but spectacular age of canal building began with the opening of the Duke of Bridgwater's Worsley to Manchester waterway in 1761. It carried coal straight from the mine to the centre of industry. The canal, it was realized, provided by far the most efficient system for carrying bulk goods and there was a frenzy of building. The pace of it was quite extraordinary, particularly as canal building was opposed by just about every vested interest – mill owners who thought they would lose their water supply, towns which were by-passed as distribution centres, and the companies which owned the turnpike toll roads which carried wagons.

By 1789, the year of the French Revolution, canals had been built connecting the Thames to the Severn estuary, the River Severn to the Trent, the Trent to the Mersey, and the Thames to the Trent. It was possible to navigate right across England, from the Channel to the Irish Sea, from the North Sea to the Atlantic. It is only subsequently that anybody has considered the ecological implications of this: at the time, the economic importance of canals for the distribution of coal and the location of industry was understandably of much greater interest.

In the 1970s, however, Alwynne Wheeler of the Natural History Museum, in a paper on the impact of industrialism on freshwater fish in Britain, came to the conclusion that canal building must have had a radical effect on fish distribution. Before the building of canals, the fact that the eastern rivers were isolated from those in the west meant that the kinds of fish to be found on the two sides of the country were different.

OPPOSITE *The fortunes of the mute swan have been greatly affected by industrialisation. Whereas the draining of wetlands and the canalising of rivers destroyed many breeding areas, gravel pit lakes have provided swans with new habitat. A ban on lead weights used by anglers has finally helped swans recover their numbers on heavily fished rivers like the Thames.*

After the last Ice Age, fish recolonized Britain in the same way as plants and land animals. When there was a land bridge to the continent, the rivers flowed through to Europe – the Humber was connected to the Rhine. Rivers in the west were further from the source of colonization and isolated earlier by the rise of the sea. Freshwater fish cannot survive long in salt water, and the sea is as effective a barrier to their migration as it is to mammals. Only migratory fish, like salmon and sea trout, sticklebacks, or those species which live in estuaries and can tolerate both salt and fresh water – flounder and smelt are examples – could cross the ocean barrier.

The result was that there were more species of purely freshwater fish on the eastern side of Britain than in the western and northern rivers. Ireland, isolated early on, had fewer species still and the roach found in the rivers there have all been introduced. They are not native, although they live very happily there – it was simply a climatological accident that they did not make it on their own.

The building of canals connected all the major rivers in England and their tributaries for the first time and would, therefore, have allowed a complete redistribution of fish, chiefly the colonization of the west and north by species from the east.

The canals themselves greatly increased the amount of freshwater in the country and though they did not have the variety of vegetation or habitat of a river, they were quickly colonized by fish such as the roach and the pike. These lay their eggs on underwater plants, and canals were always becoming overgrown with water weed, which had to be cleared when they were important for transport. Whether fish could breed in them or not, the canals were a migration route for roach, bream, tench and alien fish introduced to Britain like carp and zander.

No sooner had an extensive network of canals been built than it began to fall into decay. The railways took over from the 1840s onwards and, after a short period of bitter rivalry for trade, canals were being left undredged or cared for. Some of the smaller canals built in the 18th century have disappeared altogether, silted up and overgrown with trees. Others have been maintained and resurrected for pleasure – boating and fishing.

The rivers, too, lost their importance as transport routes and sources of power. But they were then much more seriously affected by later industrial developments, for the building of sewage systems and the siting of factories along their banks led to terrible pollution in the 19th century. Canals remained relatively clean and have possibly been of great importance in preserving stocks of fish through the worst years of river pollution. The great reservoirs formed to provide towns with drinking water have also compensated to some extent for what happened to the rivers.

One of the best documented and most remarkable histories is that of the Thames. It was a salmon river, though never one of the best, until the beginning of the 19th century. The estuary provided smelt and flounder and eels, and fishing was an important industry.

The first serious pollution arose with the invention of the water closet, and the creation of the first sewers. Before the flush toilet became popular, sewage was collected in cess pits under houses which were emptied by night soil men who carted it away to spread on the market gardens around the capital. Sewage from the water closet, in contrast, ran off into sewers which discharged into the Thames and its tributaries. The bacteria which grew on the organic matter began to consume the oxygen in the water so that it became putrid. As the metropolis grew in the 19th century, and more houses were equipped with flush toilets, the Thames became an open sewer.

A pair of tufted duck: the male is black and white. There are now an estimated 7,000 pairs of these diving ducks in Britain, a spectacular increase since the 1960s. They have done especially well on gravel pit lakes.

Salmon had disappeared by the mid-19th century. They had been affected in the early 1800s by the building of Teddington Weir to control the water flow of the river. This inhibited their journey to the spawning grounds in the upper reaches of the Thames. Sewage killed them off. Salmon require at least 30 per cent dissolved oxygen in water to survive and they could not make it from the estuary through London. Because of the strong tidal flow of the river, sewage took a long time to reach the sea and the filthy water was held for weeks in the middle stretches of the river.

The building of the Victorian sewage system eased the problem in the 1860s by shifting it down river. Massive pipes running north and south of the river carried the sewage to the east of London. The building of the London docks, too, from the early 1800s provided marginally cleaner water in which some fish survived. But the Thames got worse in the 20th century. The great expansion of inter-war suburbia, which doubled London's built-up area was served by poor and inadequate sewage works which pumped polluted water into the tributaries of the Thames. Then the bombing in the Second World War burst many of the main sewers and the river reached its biological nadir.

A study in the late 1950s found it to be more or less biologically dead for a 40-mile stretch running through the built-up area of London. Then an improvement in sewage treatment works and a concerted campaign to clean up the river began to take effect. From the 1960s the fish began to return, a discovery that came about in a most peculiar fashion.

In the inter-war years, electricity generating stations were built all along the Thames and used the water as a coolant. The most famous was the now derelict Battersea Power Station. To clear the Thames water of driftwood before it was pumped into the power stations, filters were installed. When fish began to recolonize the river, they first appeared on the power station filters. A survey was organized by Alwynne Wheeler of the Natural History Museum, counting and identifying the fish caught up on the screens. By the late 1970s the tally of fish species had reached 100 and the eel fishermen were back with their nets as far into town as Tower Bridge.

The recolonization of the river seems to have been, at least to begin with, a natural process. From the estuary came the smelt and flounder that can live in both salt and freshwater – euryhaline fish as they are called. Roach and dace and bream that had been confined to the upper reaches of the streams feeding the Thames slipped back into the main river. It was a remarkable example of the way in which the natural world could return to recolonize what had been an industrial wasteland.

Today all the power stations in London have closed down. The creation of an effective national grid system has meant that electricity does not have to be generated locally – the nearest power station to London is West Thurrock, a long way down the estuary. Now the most worrying pollutants are the residues of agricultural pesticides washed into the river from rural areas.

The story of what has happened to the lakes and rivers of Britain since the Industrial Revolution is a good example of the way in which destructive forces are compensated for quite inadvertently by the creation of new havens and new habitats. Had all the bad things – the pollution by sewage, the canalization of rivers, the build-up of pesticides, and the intensive use of rivers for transport and power – happened simultaneously, there is little doubt that much would have been wiped out. There would have been nowhere for grebes and geese, ducks, water plants and fish to go.

In the 19th century, when the Thames was so putrid the stench made Members of Parliament retch, the water was still drawn from the river for drinking. Fresh water was brought in and sold on the streets by the bucket. The solution to providing healthy drinking water for the great cities of the Victorian era was the creation of reservoirs. Most of these were built between the 1850s and the 1930s – a vast new lakeland around the metropolis which was quickly colonized by all kinds of wildfowl.

To naturalists of the time, lamenting the loss of birds from the Thames, the appearance of seagulls on the new reservoirs seemed quite miraculous and was described with a kind of awe. This is a description by C. J. Cornish in 1902 of a visit in February to Barn Elms reservoirs in West London which had been created only four years earlier:

The scene over the lakes was as sub-arctic and lacustrine as on any Finland pool, for the frost-fog hung over river and reservoirs, only just disclosing the long, flat lines of embankment, water and ice; the barges floating down with the tide were powdered with frost and snowflakes, and the only colour was the long, red smear across the ice of the western reservoir, beyond which the winter sun was setting into

OPPOSITE *A young tufted duck diving for food: midge larvae and other small creatures. When it is older it will feed on fresh water snails and mussels.*

OVERLEAF *The lagoons left by a long-abandoned shingle extraction works at Snettisham on the coast of Norfolk, which provided hardcore for US airbases during the last war, are now a haven for thousands of wintering wading birds – knot, dunlin, oyster catchers, and other birds.*

One of the more surprising exploiters of gravel pit lakes – the grass snake. It swims easily under water and can catch fish and frogs. Though it is harmless to humans, the grass snake can emit a foul smelling substance if picked up and it may feign death by lying on its back with its tongue hanging out.

a bank of snow clouds. It was four o'clock and nothing apparently was moving, either on the ice or the water, not even a gull. In the centre of the north-eastern reservoir was what was apparently an acre of heaped-up snow. On approaching nearer this acre of snow changed into a mass of gulls, all preparing to go to sleep. If there was one there were seven hundred, all packed together for warmth on the ice... Beyond the gulls, which rose and circled high above in the fog with infinite clamour, were a number of black objects, which soon resolved themselves into the forms of duck and other fowl. Rather more than seventy were counted, swimming on the water near the bank or sitting on the ice... They were not mallard, teal or widgeon; but three quarters of the number were tufted ducks... Some were approached; the whole flock rose at once and flew with arrow-like speed round the lakes and twice or thrice back over the heads of their visitors.... As several birds had not risen, we ventured still nearer and saw that most of these were coots, some ten or eleven, which did not fly but ran out on to the ice. Two large birds remaining, which had dived, then rose to the surface, and to our surprise and pleasure proved to be great crested grebes.

By 1945, when Richard Fitter wrote his celebrated *London's Natural History*, Barn Elms – and many of the other reservoirs – had become meccas for bird watchers who would see much greater numbers and variety of wildfowl than excited Cornish in 1902. An island in Walthamstow reservoirs now has one of the largest heron colonies in the country and during the winter cormorant fish there for trout introduced by anglers.

The rivers of England have now, to a large extent, lost their economic importance and there is a greater opportunity for them to be returned to something like a natural state than at any time in the past two centuries. The canals, too, are redundant, as are the reservoirs created to top up the flow of water in them. So far, the record of industrialism on fish populations and wildfowl has not been nearly as damaging as one might imagine.

But, just as the gravel pits, reservoirs, canals and rivers have arisen or been resurrected to freshwater creatures, the natural wetlands of Britain have begun to disappear at an unprecedented rate. Industry has provided the machinery and the wealth to drain farming land that had remained sodden and regularly flooded for centuries. The new habitats do not compensate in full for the loss of the old, for they have less diversity of vegetation and a poorer food supply.

In time, flooded gravel pits will become richer in species and, with careful conservation management, they can be made much more valuable in a short space of time than those pits simply left to develop in their own way. Plants which cannot colonize naturally can be introduced; the depth and the shoreline can be sculpted with bulldozers; artificial islands which provide breeding sanctuaries for birds can be created.

The conflicts between people and wildlife continue: gravel pits are colonized quickly by anglers as well as fish, windsurfers as well as wildfowl. But then, sanctuaries put aside exclusively for wildlife will always be exceptional; the demand for space is too great. What is indisputable is the fact that most wild creatures and plants can survive and thrive in this crowded island however much the landscape is rearranged. And one of the most extraordinary stories is told in the next chapter – the way war has helped preserve much threatened wildlife.

3 The Blasted Heath

Salisbury Plain is one of the strangest places in the country. Stonehenge, like a Druid doodle in stone, gives it a mysticism and the low undulation of the landscape, with its scattered woodland and chalk grasslands, appears mysteriously archaic. Where the farmed land ends and the downs begin there is a sharp, visual change even in winter, the arable fields a bright carpet of green, the rough grazed grass a tufted rug. All the time you hear a booming, distant but massive. Red flags fly and out on the grassland a cluster of shrubs will suddenly wobble and begin to move. The Army, stalking an imaginary enemy, is on manoeuvres. Then the sky is torn with the horrendous roar of a jet fighter, buckling the air with its thrust low over the ground, then rising almost to vanishing point. Sometimes, in the distance, there is a shower of billowy little mushrooms from droning aircraft as the Army makes a parachute drop.

A woman out riding, two dogs snuffling up ahead, puts up short-eared owls which lope off with their bouncy almost butterfly-like flight. You might meet a falconer flying peregrines against partridge, and the local pack of beagles like something from a circus sniffing out hares. In summer, orchids bloom on the chalk, never in the arable fields, always on the grassland. And in the devastated impact area of the artillery ranges, local naturalists turn out on the few days when the firing stops to watch badgers which have dug their setts among the craters and roe deer, which graze on the plain quite unconcerned about the guns. Today the Army owns about 90,000 acres in Wiltshire. Some of the land they let to farmers on different arrangements – cheap but liable to be the scene of a mock battle, or a proper rent and mostly out of bounds to the military.

The rest of the Salisbury Plain land is used exclusively for military training. At Larkhill there is the artillery school and a whole series of camps where regiments stay to practise the modern art of warfare. The military areas of the Plain are of much greater value to wildlife than any of the farming land around. The disturbance of guns and tanks and jet fighters is of little concern to birds or mammals, and the preservation of woodland and sheep-grazed grasslands for military manoeuvres has ensured the survival of a kind of habitat which would otherwise have disappeared from Wiltshire and has become increasingly scarce in the country as a whole.

There is no more bizarre story in the history of wildlife in Britain since the Industrial Revolution than the discovery that Ministry of Defence land is a superb and extremely valuable haven for many plants and animals that are threatened elsewhere. Since the 1970s, when there was great pressure to reduce the amount of land controlled by the Services and to make more of it open to the public, the M.O.D. has recognized the publicity value of its wildlife reserves. There is a peculiar affinity between the sort of terrain the Army needs for its training and a range of habitat which is especially good for a range of threatened wildlife.

It is not entirely by chance that this has come about. When the Army first began to look for training grounds and firing ranges, it naturally chose some of the most sparsely inhabited and wildest parts of the country. And, once it had established itself there, the dangers of military activity meant that the public had

OPPOSITE *The adder and the soldier. By a quirk of historical fate the army in search of training grounds has become the custodian of some of the most valuable habitat in Britain, especially heathland. Longmoor camp, south of Aldershot, is home to all the reptiles and amphibians in the country.*

to be excluded. For the past century and a half, the expansion of defence lands has, therefore, run counter to all other social and economic pressures.

From the 1850s, the first steps were taken in the creation of a truly professional Army in Britain. Garrison towns, military training and the testing of weapons had taken place long before that. But the Army did not own much land and was not organized in any recognizably modern fashion. The testing of weapons did not require anything like the acreage needed today, when field guns can fire so far – up to twelve miles – that they have to take into account the spin of the earth when calculating the trajectory of a shell. In the 17th century, guns were tested on the site of what is now Liverpool Street station in London, before they moved to Moorfields and what is still called Artillery Lane. Everything was on a much smaller scale and much more haphazard. Before the Battle of Waterloo in 1815, military manoeuvres would be carried out on land rented temporarily from landowners.

The amateurishness and backwardness of Army training was revealed tragically in the Crimean War, when fox-hunting dandies like Lord Cardigan led absurd cavalry charges against guns which simply mowed them down. Until that time, it was the conventional wisdom that chasing foxes on horseback was damn good training for a cavalry officer, and most hunts had a special place for the young bloods of the Army. The realization that this was not adequate came with Crimea, and the replacement of the Duke of Wellington by a new Commander-in-Chief, Lord Hardinge, in 1851 who paved the way for innovation which the Iron Duke had resisted.

Hardinge had taken the first steps to acquire a permanent military training ground just before Crimea. He was greatly encouraged by Prince Albert who was very interested in military strategy and it is possible the choice of the first site for a military camp was influenced by the fact that he could easily reach it from Windsor.

Lord Hardinge's search for a training ground took him to the Red Lion Inn at Aldershot, then a small village with a population of about 1,000. The surrounding heathland seemed ideal and, in an atmosphere of war fever, the go-ahead was given in 1854 for the purchase of 10,000 acres to form the Army's first-ever permanent camp. It was, by all accounts, a mucky and insalubrious beginning, for the village of Aldershot became a boom town as the first tents were put up and construction workers moved in. Drunkenness and prostitution quickly became endemic and an eyewitness at the time described the effect on the landscape:

> *Take a highwayman's heath. Destroy every vestige of life with fire and axes, from the pine which has longest been a landmark, to the smallest beetle smothered in smoking moss. Burn acres of purple and pink heather, pare away the young bracken that springs verdant from its ashes. Let flame consume the perfumed gorse in all its glory and not spare the broom, whose more exquisite yellow atones for its lack of fragrance ... by some such recipe the ground was prepared for the camp of Construction.*

The first invasion of wild heathland by the Army was clearly traumatic for wildlife, as well as for the local villagers. But the setting up of Aldershot began a long period of acquisition by the Army of heathland and downland which was in the mid-19th century losing its economic value in a nation which had become essentially urban and which relied less and less on heaths for gathering fuel or grazing animals. It was very useful to the War Office that heathland was going out of fashion for the price they had to pay to acquire it was correspondingly low. Aldershot Heath cost £12 per acre.

OPPOSITE *A smooth snake close to the scene of a mock battle at Longmoor Camp. These snakes are confined to heathlands where they stalk their prey, lizards and small mammals, and kill by constriction. Smooth snakes have no poison.*

The Aldershot heaths were not sufficient for the Army as it was reorganized and engaged in more and more large-scale reviews and training exercises in the second half of the 19th century. It sometimes needed areas of several square miles for exercises – what became known as manoeuvres. In 1871, 32,769 troops took part in such an exercise at Aldershot. Everything in those days was horse-drawn and elaborate arrangements had to be made for feeding and watering the animals. In 1872 there were manoeuvres on Salisbury Plain, and the following year on Dartmoor, but as the Army did not own the land, the permissions required to allow so many soldiers and horses to trundle about made them very cumbersome. A Military Lands Act was passed in 1892.

It is odd that the great expansion of military training grounds should have taken place during a period in British history when the country was not engaged in a major war – the so-called Century of Peace. But the British Empire was expanding rapidly and entering its most intense period of jingoism, the New Imperialist era, and the Army was called upon more and more to enforce law and order in the colonies. A study of the hostilities that took place during Queen Victoria's reign (1837–1901) arrived at a grand total of 165 – 36 wars, 18 campaigns, 98 expeditions and 13 operations. This did not include a great many sieges, insurrections, disturbances, rebellions and uprisings. At the same time, the technology of war was evolving very rapidly, and there was – as there is today – a fear of being left behind in the arms race by potentially belligerent neighbours in Europe.

The long tailed fieldmouse thrives in rough grasslands and is one of the inhabitants of the impact zone of the artillery firing ranges on Salisbury Plain.

The first 40,000 acres of Salisbury Plain were bought by the Army in 1897, under the new powers of the Military Lands Acts – several of which had been passed by then. It was acquired bit by bit, the total cost just topping £500,000. The Wiltshire downlands had a number of attractions for the Army. Most of the area was unenclosed – it had not been fenced off and carved up into fields during the great period of Parliamentary Enclosure in the previous century. It was dry chalk downland which would not be easily churned to mud by horses and gun carriages. As it was mainly sheep-grazing land, it had no great agricultural value. And it was in a reasonably strategic place, not far from Aldershot, London or the coast at Southampton.

Local reaction to the announcement that the Army was moving into the area seems to have been favourable – it would bring a new source of wealth to a region with declining farming fortunes. No thought at all was given to the wildlife of the Plain, except from the point of view of hunting and the problem of rabbits. In the year Tedworth Estate was bought by the Army, 14,000 rabbits had been killed on it. The Plain was pitted with rabbit holes which were a hazard for cavalry as the horses were liable to stumble on them. One of the Army's first assaults was on the rabbit population, which included a plan – later abandoned – to fill in all the holes by hand. The estimate that it would take twenty men one month to complete the task made it too costly and tenant farmers were instructed to keep the rabbits down.

Of more interest to the hunting men in the military were the Tedworth fox hounds which had been established in the early 19th century, and the sport of beagling. The chalk downland of the Plain was wonderful habitat for hares and these provided the Royal Artillery (Bulford) Harriers, a beagle pack formed in 1907, with plenty of sport. You will still see the beagle packs out on the Plain, an anachronistic band, quite comical in the vastness of the place.

The value of these military sites was not really recognized until after the last war when the kind of territory they occupied was becoming, in ecological terms, a dangerously scarce resource. And though individuals in the Forces had taken an interest in wildlife, there was no official recognition of its importance until a report of the Defence Lands Committee in 1971–73 which led to the appointment of a Conservation Officer and the setting up of conservation groups. These try to reconcile the sometimes conflicting interests of wildlife, archaeology and military training. Today, a large part of the Ministry of Defence landholdings of 660,000 acres is of conservation value, a considerable amount within the boundaries of the National Parks. Of the four to five thousand designated Sites of Special Scientific Interest, nearly 200 are on Ministry of Defence land.

All three Services have some land for training but the Army is by far the biggest user, with a great variety of sites from the ranges of Shoeburyness on the Thames Estuary to the tank firing ranges of Lulworth Cove in Dorset.

In southern England, among the most valuable ecological sites is the first ever acquired at Aldershot. The kind of heath preserved here has been fast disappearing, not only in lowland Britain but in northern Europe – Sweden and Denmark – as well. Its history is especially interesting for it illustrates the extent to which valuable habitat has been, and still is, very much dependent on the social and economic history of the country.

There is a puzzle about the history of heathlands and the species of plant and animal it harbours. If nearly all of Britain and northern Europe was wooded or swampy before the felling of the trees began several thousand years ago, where did the heathland species live – all the snakes and lizards and the birds which like to nest in and hunt over open country, like the stone curlew or the hobby, a

The stone curlew is one of the shyest and rarest birds in Britain, nesting close to the firing ranges on Salisbury Plain and in Breckland in East Anglia.

small falcon that catches dragonflies as well as sand martins and swallows?

There were natural heaths on thin acid soils where the treeline ended, high on the mountains, and along the most windswept coasts. They must have been isolated patches which were colonized after the last Ice Age, as the temperature rose and the tundra below the ice sheets began to turn to woodland. Most of the studies of the origins of lowland heathland in Britain and northern Europe have concluded that they were at one time woodland and reverted to heath either because of the felling of trees or a climatic cooling which did not favour tree growth, or a combination of the two forces working together. Everybody agrees that there would not have been nearly so much heathland, surviving for so long, had it not been managed in a particular way by man. The fact that much of it has quickly turned to woodland when left untended is sufficient proof of this.

The most up-to-date work on heathlands in southern England has come to the conclusion that much of it was created, in the first instance, by peat cutting for fuel. This thinned the soils, which were then kept clear of trees by the grazing of cattle and sheep. Heaths were unfenced and the animals allowed to wander. Each year part of it would be burned to promote the growth of new heather shoots for the animals to feed on. The burning would obviously kill off some animals, but if the heath was extensive there would be a healthy enough population of any species to recolonize the burned areas.

The most characteristic plant of heathland – heather – thrives with regular burning which suggests that it is a species with an evolutionary adaptation to scorched earth. Like a great many plants which have become scarce in the era of modern intensive agriculture, it thrives where the soil is poor for its root system can cope with these conditions and there is less competition from other plants trying to muscle in. Heather is known to botanists, rather unflatteringly, as a dwarf shrub adapted to some of the grimmest climatic and geological landscapes in north-west Europe.

Heathlands are valued today by conservationists not only because they are habitat for many rare species but because they represent such a contrast to areas of intensive farming. They appear to be primeval wildernesses, whereas they were created by soil erosion in the past.

Mountains and moors were first praised by the poets and travel writers towards the end of the 18th century – as a reaction to agricultural improvement in England, especially farming was becoming much more organized and the former wastes were being ploughed up. The common fields had given way in the Midlands to the orderliness of enclosure, and two million acres of ground were brought into regular cultivation. At the end of the 17th century, the writer Gregory King estimated that out of 39 million acres in the country (he was two million over the true figure) 10 million were heaths, mountains and barren land. This was the great age of agricultural improvement and propagandists for more efficient farming like Arthur Young who wanted to cover the wastelands with 'turnips, corn and clover, instead of ling, whins and fern'. William Cobbett wrote of 'rascally heaths'. The travel writer William Gilpin remarked that the generality of people did not like wild nature and that 'there are few who do not prefer the busy scenes of cultivation to the greatest of nature's rough productions'.

In his *Tour through the Whole Island of Great Britain*, written in the 1720s, Daniel Defoe had this to say of the Surrey heaths, so prized and worried over by conservationists today:

> *Much of it is a sandy desert, where winds raise the sands . . . This sand indeed is checked by the heath, or heather, which grows in it, and which is the common product of barren land, even in the very highlands of Scotland, but the ground is otherwise so poor and barren, that the product of it feeds no creatures, but some very small sheep, who feed chiefly on the said heather, and but very few of these, nor are there any villages worth remembering, and but few houses, or people for many miles far and wide; this desert lies extended so much that some say there is not less than a hundred thousand acres of this barren land that lies all together, reaching out every way in the three counties of Surrey, Hampshire and Berkshire.*

It is quite probable that these barren heaths were the product of soil erosion following on forest clearance which took place several thousand years ago. Characteristically, the soil of heathlands is podsolized, that is to say the nutrients are washed out from the topsoil so that it can support few species of plant. This means that it is not so much rich in wildlife, as a very specialized kind of habitat for some rare species which do not do as well on lusher ground.

In particular, the heathlands provide a home for Britain's tiny range of reptiles – there are only six of these cold-blooded creatures which are native. These are the common lizard, the sand lizard, the smooth snake, the slow worm, the grass snake and the adder or viper. The belief is that these all colonized Britain from Europe when there was still a land bridge at the end of the last Ice Age, but then suffered when the climate turned colder about 5,000 years ago.

A barn owl perched on a burned out tank in the impact zone of the Salisbury Plain firing ranges. Barn owls have been declining during this century, probably because of the use of poisons to kill rats and mice on farmland. The unsprayed grasslands of the firing ranges are a last refuge: shellfire is less damaging to wildlife than chemical weaponry.

The creation of heathlands, open sandy-soiled country in which they could bask and soak up the warmth of the sun provided them with an artificially warm habitat at the very northern end of their European range. In recent times the disappearance of heathland has put them under pressure, though only two of these reptiles are really confined to heath. The adder, the grass snake, the slow worm and the common lizard all live quite well in other kinds of habitat. It is the sand lizard and the smooth snake which need the arid, open sandy country of the heath.

It is indicative of how much our knowledge of natural history of this country has increased in the past two centuries that the smooth snake was not identified until the Victorian period when naturalists out looking for insects near Bournemouth stumbled across it in 1853. A published account of the snake a few years later set the Victorian naturalists on its trail and it was found on heathlands in many parts of southern England, at just the point in its history when it was probably on the decline.

The smooth snake is not poisonous but constricts its prey, which might be the young of mammals like voles or shrews, or lizards. It needs a sandy soil in which it can burrow and appears to favour sandy heaths with heather and gorse, but not a great deal is known about its behaviour. One reason it has become, and remains, rare is that its breeding success is poor in British conditions which do not appear to be quite warm enough.

One of the rarest and strangest creatures in Britain, the natterjack toad. It is distinguished by a yellow stripe down its back and loud croaking during the breeding season. The natterjack comes out at night, and digs itself into sand during the day. It is confined now to a few protected sites – one of them at Longmoor Camp on the Surrey heaths.

Sand lizards similarly are at the northern edge of their range and need the warmth of sandy heaths in which to soak up heat and to lay their eggs. They eat insects and spiders and appear to favour heaths with a range of dwarf shrubs.

Both the sand lizard and the smooth snake lay eggs – they are in the jargon oviparous. The other four reptiles are all viviparous – they give birth to live young. It may be this factor above all which restricts the range of the first two to heathland, as they require sandy soil in which to lay their eggs.

Of the six amphibians native to Britain – three kinds of newt, two toads and one frog – only one is really confined to heathlands, although this is often a good habitat for the others as well. The heathland specialist is the oddly named Natterjack Toad, which is one of those creatures which appears to have a lifestyle quite unsuited to survival in a rugged world. Unlike the more familiar frog or the common toad, the Natterjack likes sandy areas in which it can burrow. However, though it does burrow, the Natterjack does not have limbs specially modified to perform this task. In addition, it does not do well if its shallow breeding pools are too acidic, and lots of heathland pools are acid. The natterjack feeds on beetles and larvae of moths and butterflies.

Nobody is quite sure why the Natterjack is doing so badly in its traditional strongholds of sand dune and heath, for its decline seems to be much more rapid than the shrinking of its favoured habitat. One possible explanation is the decline of rabbits since myxomatosis struck in 1953, for much grassland and heathland is less intensively grazed and the vegetation has grown higher and shadier – not something the Natterjack likes.

One of the more touching stories in the recent history of such endangered wildlife in this country is the way in which the Army has been involved in nurturing a colony of Natterjack Toads on the heathlands of Longmoor Camp near Aldershot. Shallow ponds have been scooped for them to breed in, and brick tiles have been scattered about to provide ready-made shelters for the toads to scuttle under. In fact, the heathlands of Longmoor where Army battalions practise rifle fire, manoeuvres, make parachute drops and train for the guerilla warfare of Northern Ireland in a few abandoned streets of former married quarters, has a quite extraordinary list of species.

All British amphibians and reptiles are found here. The sand lizards and smooth snakes live where they make parachute drops on the drier sandy areas. The various ponds and lakes have grass snakes, frogs and common toads. The adder, too, manages to survive despite the military activity. As with other sensitive sites, a conservation group of Army and wildlife specialists reviews the impact of training on the flora and fauna of the heaths.

Among the birds here are sand martins. Unlike house martins, which are common town birds, the sand martins need for their nesting site a sandy cliff face into which they burrow to build their nests. At Longmoor Camp their favoured spot is the pistol range. Similarly an increasingly rare bird, the wood lark, favours for its nest sites the bleak landscape in and around the FIBUA (Fighting in Built Up Areas) zone of the abandoned married quarters.

Another rare bird which regularly nests on these military heaths is a little falcon, the hobby. It hunts dragonflies and large insects over the heathlands, as well as swallows and martins. The hobby does not build its own nest, but takes over an old crow's nest, often in a pine tree close to the heathland hunting ground. There are thought to be 500 pairs of hobbies nesting each year in southern England, mostly on heathland but sometimes in farmland areas as well. It arrives as a summer migrant in April or May from its wintering territory in Africa. The hobby is not in danger of extinction in Britain, though it is thought

OPPOSITE *The pistol range at Longmoor Camp. An amphitheatre cut in a sandy hill has proved to be ideal for sandmartins which have excavated their nests and raised their young with no concern for the constant rattle of gunfire.*

that its numbers have declined with the disappearance of heathland. One factor in its favour is that it hunts for the most part over land which has not been contaminated by the pesticides of modern farming. Several pairs of hobby nest on the military heathlands of Longmoor Camp each year.

Not all heathlands are quite the same in ecological terms: some are dry, some are wet, some are sandy, some more peaty. Those in the extreme south-west, and the extensive but dwindling Dorset Heaths in particular, have a warmer, moister climate and harbour the largest British populations of those sensitive species that are right on the edge of their European range. Among these are the Dartford Warbler and the nightjar. Both are quite common on the continent, but are dependent on the preservation of this special habitat if they are to survive in Britain.

If there were no need today for military training areas much of the heathland around Longmoor Camp, would undoubtedly have disappeared. And if wild animals did not have a quite extraordinary tolerance of the noise and disturbance of gunfire, the tramping of troops and noisy Army vehicles, these areas would have little value for conservation. But the birds have learned that though there is a great deal of firing going on, nobody is aiming at them. On the rifle ranges, carrion crows quite often fly across while firing is going on, and will scavenge around the targets when the firing stops.

The colony of sandmartins at Longmoor pistol range is growing, but nationally these birds have suffered a serious decline, probably because of a shortage of nest sites.

A proof of the nonchalance of birds was beautifully illustrated on one occasion in early summer. A team of Army Air Corps soldiers were engaged in rifle training, running 50 yards or so to their firing positions and blasting at targets which popped up at various distances. The hail of bullets kicks up sand at the back of the range. The firing positions are marked with wooden posts, about three feet high. While the firing was going on, a woodlark sat singing on one of

Sand martins in their nest, excavated in the sandy cliffs of Surrey heathlands. These are summer migrants from Africa.

the outside posts. Then it would hop to the ground just to the left of the line of fire and join its mate feeding young. In the pauses between firing, the family of woodlarks would move across in front of the firing positions, pecking at worms and insects, and sometimes singing. They were more disturbed by a camera crew trying to film them behaving in this remarkable way than they were by the gunfire.

Woodlarks, which for some reason favour burned ground for their nest sites, regularly choose the FIBUA to raise their young. Blue tits nest in the pipes of the battered houses and starlings continue to fly in and out feeding young right through the cacophony of mock battles. There are rabbits everywhere too, around the edge of the FIBUA.

But the most remarkable scene at Longmoor is on the pistol range, which is used for practice with rapid fire sub-machine guns as well. The ground here is pure sand, and an amphitheatre has been cut into a low hill, creating walls of sand on three sides. In the deepest part of this giant sand pit are the targets, riddled with bullet holes. And to the left, between 20 to 30 metres from the targets, are the holes excavated by a colony of sandmartins. In this setting, the honeycomb of nests looks at first like the pock marks of artillery fire in a castle wall. Then the sandmartins descend in a flitting mass, and shoot into them, chirruping. Sometimes the flock of birds weaves around for a minute or two just above the targets, and appear to be dodging the hail of gunfire.

The artillery ranges and training areas of Salisbury Plain are quite different from those at Longmoor Camp. Here, the largest tank manoeuvres in Britain are staged on dry, rolling chalk grasslands. And the big guns of the artillery school at Larkhill boom all day. In the spring and early summer there is a most peculiar mix of sounds. Intermittently there is the crump of a distant gun, the eerie whistle of the shell, and the faint crack of an explosion far away in the impact area. The noise of the firing punctuates the continuous trilling of larks as they rise from the downland grass, hovering and spiralling into the sky. When tanks are out on the Plain, the larks flit around them, and you can see them feeding in the deep indents of the caterpillar tracks.

Even a large-scale tank exercise, which does some damage to the ground and fills the air with exhaust fumes and the clanking and grinding of engines, disturbs the wildlife of the Plain very little. At dawn, a roe buck will appear, prancing between the tanks parked in the mist like a prehistoric beast. It may hide for a while in a young conifer copse, running back towards the tanks and then disappear into the distance as the sun rises.

The most remarkable sight on Salisbury Plain, however, is the wildlife of the impact area. It is a vast expanse of chalk downland blasted constantly by shellfire, and marked Danger Zone in bold red letters on all maps. Because of the risk of misfiring, it is cordoned off from the public for miles around the target area. The impact zone is the remotest and bleakest piece of countryside in modern Britain. And it is full of wildlife which appears to value the lack of disturbance from the dog-walking public far more than it fears the continual explosion of shells. Roe deer graze the long grass here, and badgers have dug their setts amid the battered target tanks, and trundle over craters in search of food. From time to time, some of this intrepid wildlife must be accidentally blown to pieces but – like Londoners in the Blitz – the deer and badgers, the butterflies and hares, appear to take the stalwart view that their show should go on.

The silver studded blue butterfly is confined to heaths which have been disappearing from central and southern England. Army training grounds provide it with a last refuge.

Mad march hares chasing and boxing in a field of winter wheat on the edges of the Salisbury Plain military training area. The chalk grasslands on which the hares thrive has been preserved here for tank manoeuvres. Elsewhere, hares appear to be in decline, possibly because of the great increase in the fox population of the country.

This is true not just on Salisbury Plain, but on many Ministry of Defence sites around the country. On the sandy heaths of Breckland in East Anglia; the bombing ranges of the coast near the Wash; the tank firing areas at Lulworth Cove in Dorset; on the shingle coast at Shoeburyness on the Thames estuary. All these places have been recognized for years as superb places for wildlife, partly because the military has naturally chosen wild uninhabited places in which to rehearse for warfare, and because, in doing so, it has preserved certain habitats as they were and held at bay the forces which have so altered otherwise peaceful parts of the countryside.

In a way which is pleasing for anyone with a liking for the absurd, the modern demands of warfare have made the Ministry of Defence custodians of a great deal of rare wildlife. And though it is frequently in conflict with conservationists who dislike the rearrangement of the landscape for military purposes, the MOD has come to recognize that its wild plants and animals are a powerful ally whenever there is public pressure for it to release some of its land, or make it more accessible to the public. As guardians of such threatened species as the stone curlew, which inhabits the most barren, stony ground, the military is able to argue that wildlife and warfare have a special affinity, and with considerable justification.

Though the conservation value of firing ranges and Army training grounds is a special case of the demands of industrial society inadvertently favouring wildlife, there is a more general principle here too. Wherever land is exploited not primarily for farming, there are likely to be special benefits for wild plants and animals. And this has been true historically, in a variety of ways, where the management of the countryside has been greatly influenced by those seeking pleasure – in particular for hunting and shooting. In many ways this is even more surprising than the affinity between the military and wildlife, for the pursuit of field sports involves people shooting directly at birds and other animals, rather than at other people – sometimes a cavalry charge more than a hundred strong against an 'enemy' which is no bigger than a small dog.

4 Moveable Beasts

It is difficult to grasp at first what an absurd sport fox-hunting is, and even harder to understand why the well-to-do in England should have become so obsessed with it in the Victorian period. As contemporaries noted, the fox is not only inedible, it is generally regarded in the countryside as vermin, a pest to be kept under control and, if possible, eliminated. And there is no less efficient way of catching foxes than pursuing them in broad daylight with a pack of thirty or more hounds followed by a mounted field, resplendent in red and black coats, numbering upwards of one hundred. The cost of this cavalry charge might run into thousands of pounds, and certainly did in the 19th century, whereas many more foxes could be shot or snared for a few shillings than the most successful meet could catch up with in a season.

The ritual of fox-hunting cannot be understood in purely rational terms, though even today those who defend the sport against the charge that it is cruel still try to argue that they are performing a necessary job of pest control. That is not the point of fox-hunting today, and it never was. It is a sport like any other and what distinguishes it from most is the enormous expense involved. That was always one of its great attractions, for to be able to hunt six days a week in the season, you had to be wealthy – a gentleman or gentlewoman. The exclusiveness of hunting was one of the keys to its astonishing popularity in the 19th century, for its invention and spread throughout the country was to a large extent a reaction to the social changes brought about by the rise of industrialism.

Fox-hunting was only one manifestation of the way in which the well-to-do and the landed aristocracy in particular reacted to industrialism and, in doing so, had a tremendous impact both on the landscape of Britain and its wildlife. To a large extent, those who owned the land treated it as a playground as well as a source of wealth and managed and manipulated it for their own pleasure. Tenant farmers on the big estates were expected to raise crops and livestock without interfering with the squirearchy's sport, whether it was the local hunt thundering through their fences and churning up their fields, or the shooting parties that wanted plenty of rabbit, hare, partridge or pheasant to pot at. The fact that game species ate all the tenant farmers' crops and foxes preyed on lambs and chickens was considered of no consequence by a Parliament of land owners who more and more got their wealth from mineral rights and selling land to railways and from trade.

In the second half of the 19th century, the exploitation of wildlife for the pleasure of the wealthy reached its absurd apotheosis as they defied every axiom of ecology in their efforts to dress out the countryside with a range of species that would give them pleasure. This was the heyday not only of the highly organized shooting of game driven over rapid fire shotguns, and of fox-hunting, but of the introductions of new species from other parts of the world to top up the stock of game to provide the wealthy with amusingly exotic creatures in their parks. Not a great deal of new technology was required for this jamboree of experimentation, but there were critical innovations which made it possible. The railways enabled the leisured classes to attend Parliament, or some social

OPPOSITE *The red fox became a sacred animal for the upper classes in the eighteenth century, and was bought and sold to provide sport. The result has been a great increase in the number of foxes in the country. It is now a popular symbol of wildlife in modern Britain.*

occasion in the evening, after a day in the field on a country estate. And steamships made the transportation of exotic wildlife from other parts of the world much more practical.

But the driving force behind it all was more subtle, involving a change in the outlook of the wealthy and a reaction to the industrial developments which both increased their fortunes enormously and threatened in the long run to undermine the basis of their wealth and political power. It is not entirely illogical that wildlife got caught up in all this, for certain chosen creatures have always been associated with privilege and made the exclusive property of Kings and the most powerful barons in the land.

Before fox-hunting became popular, the beasts of the chase were the deer and the hare. Foxes were hunted but not by people on horseback – they were tracked down early in the morning in their earths. Nobody chased them across the countryside because they were far too fast for the dogs, which were called harriers. These were bred for their acute sense of smell which was what was needed for chasing hares which tried to escape not by covering a large distance very fast, but by constantly doubling back on the same ground.

Though deer were hunted with staghounds, they were scarce even in the late Middle Ages and were confined in parks so that they could not roam freely around the countryside. There were many different ways of hunting them, and chasing them on horseback seems to have been neither the most practical nor the most popular form of pursuit. Elizabeth I, in her later years, would have the stag driven inside a park so that she and her courtiers could shoot it down with crossbows. There is a record of a deer hunt at Cowdray Park in 1591 at which the Queen shot four deer while her musicians played and sang. The hard ride on horseback with a pack of hounds was, it seems, a French courtly tradition which was favoured by Henry VIII and by Shakespeare. But that required the survival of very large tracts of land, and good stocks of deer, and many of the deer parks of the minor aristocracy would not have been large enough for such a chase. One of the great pleasures of hunting on horseback is the breaking of conventional boundaries of land-ownership, and this is true of fox-hunting even today – the freedom to trample over the landscape without any idea where you will end up is part of the emotional liberation of the chase.

Stag-hunting did continue as fox-hunting began to take over, but it was less and less fashionable, and in the end became ludicrous for the deer had to be 'carted' to the spot where they were to be chased and by the 20th century were sometimes preserved from the kill so they could be hunted again. The carting of deer began around 1728, but it was the beginning of the end. Deer hunting continued in the suburban areas around London into the 19th century, but it became an embarrassment with the quarry running through market gardens and taking refuge in conservatories, and reputedly in people's living rooms on occasions. One of the last stag hunters was a chap called Grantley Berkley, who kept hounds near London in the early 19th century.

Raymond Carr in *English Fox-Hunting* quotes Lord Alvanley on a day out with Grantley Berkley. He was asked in White's Club how it had gone; 'Devilish good run,' he replied, 'but the asparagus beds went awfully heavy; and the grass all through was up to one's hocks.' That hunt came to an end in 1829, by which time fox-hunting was far more popular and salubrious. There is still stag-hunting on Exmoor in the west of England, and stag hounds occasionally turn out to run after fallow deer in the New Forest, but it has long been an anachronism.

The modern form of fox-hunting first began to take shape in 1753 when a wealthy young man called Hugo Meynell rented Quorndon Hall in Leicestershire and began to breed a new kind of hunting dog, the foxhound. These were much faster than the harriers that ran after hares, and were followed in the field on horseback. The great thrill was in the sudden bursts of speed that were possible, the hard riding across country. Meynell was a fashionable chap, known in London society, and began to give fox-hunting an élan it had not previously enjoyed.

What Hugo Meynell devised was a more genuinely rural and exciting sport, and he chose a part of the country which had, in the 18th century, become ideally suited to the gallop over fields. In the Midlands and parts of southern England, agricultural improvements had taken the form of Parliamentary Enclosure of fields. It was a form of daylight robbery perpetrated on the rural communities of these areas, for through Act of Parliament the land that they tilled was taken away from them and put into the ownership of individuals who turned the open, arable fields and heaths into pasture, divided up by hedgerows. Thousands of miles of hawthorn hedges were planted.

The acres of turf provided the ideal terrain for chasing foxes across country. Meynell himself was not that keen on jumping hedges but, in time, the cross-country steeplechase became a big part of the attraction of fox-hunting. Quorndon Hall became the centre for this new form of hunting and the most famous hunt in the country remains the Quorn. As more and more of the upper classes were attracted to the new sport, the town of Melton Mowbray – famous also for pork pies – became the mecca of fox-hunting as people travelled to spend some time with the most celebrated packs of hounds in the country.

Fox cubs emerge from their burrow or earth in the Spring and can often be seen playing in broad daylight. They have a very varied diet which is one of the reasons they have thrived in the countryside and suburbia of modern Britain.

The status of the fox began to change rapidly. In the 17th century it was said:

> *We give law to hares and deer, because they are beasts of the chase: it was never accounted either cruelty or foul play to knock foxes and wolves on the head as they can be found, because they are beasts of prey.*

In the late 18th century, it became quite unacceptable in the countryside to knock a fox on the head – what was known as vulpicide (the fox's Latin name is *Vulpes Vulpes*). By the time fox hunting had become *the* sport of the upper classes in the mid-19th century, battle was joined between hunters and farmers over the issue of killing foxes. The hunting dukes would write critically to any land owner if they heard that tenant farmers on the land were interfering with the foxes. The Duke of Cleveland's agent wrote as follows to two landlords in the area of his hunt:

> *I feel quite sure you would not allow a tenant of yours to damage the sport of others. Your estate is a resort of foxes in the breeding season, which in a fox-hunting district makes it most desirable they should meet with fair play or a whole country may be spoilt*

> *There has been foul play with foxes . . . an unlooked-for and shameful outrage that has taken place in a fox-hunting country . . . a tenant of yours has made it his business to destroy foxes on Anniscliffe Moor.*

The term 'country' here refers to the division of rural areas into territories which were the preserve of particular hunts. By the mid-19th century, most of England had been carved up in this way, and within their own 'countries' the hunting aristocracy would go to great lengths to ensure a good supply of foxes.

The whole of the countryside in the territory of a hunt was looked upon as a vast playground, or steeplechase course, and pressure was brought to bear on farms to maintain hedges and fences so that they were easily and safely jumped. Many patches of woodland and gorse were planted. This had, and still has, the dual purpose of retaining foxes by providing them with a covert, a place to lie up during the day, and ensuring that the hunt knows where to go to look for them – the 'draw'.

In this way, the landscape of a large part of the central and southern parts of England was shaped in the 18th and 19th centuries – it is impossible to understand it without a knowledge of fox-hunting. Even today, when fox-hunting has lost much of its social prestige, you can see in Leicestershire the well-preserved hedges and the spinneys which are retained for the hunt. The advent of barbed wire in the latter half of the 19th century caused a crisis in hunting for it was lethal when hidden in hedges, and today the jumpable places are marked with a small red and white wooden flag in the hedge. There are also gaps known as 'tiger traps' which are specially designed jumpable fences.

The coming of the railways carved up a lot of the newly-formed hunt 'countries' and caused some bitter arguments, for the hounds could not be allowed to run across the lines. But, in the long run, steam trains added to the popularity of fox hunting and the number of packs rose from 99 in 1850 to 137 in 1877. What society people discovered was that, with the speed of the railways, they could travel out to a good bit of hunting country, horses and all, and back in a day. Ladies began to join the hunt as well, so that by the 1860s it was very much a part of the social round. The old school of hard-riding hunters began to lament the disappearance of the days when everyone rode hard and the advent of a large, effete field that simply looked smart, chattered constantly and shied away from any fences.

Fox-hunting was justified on the grounds that it brought the whole of the rural community together in a common pursuit and historians have generally agreed that it did have a remarkable influence in its heyday. Country life was changing rapidly, industrial wealth was beginning to usurp landed wealth and rural communities were dying as poorer people moved into towns. Fox-hunting was said to make the countryside attractive to society people who might otherwise not have left town in winter. And the hunt itself brought all social classes together, providing a focus for the community. Though there was truth in this, fox-hunting was really a throwback to an earlier era in the history of the countryside, an invented 'tradition' celebrating a 'community' of squires and tenants held together not by equality but by deference. The massive inefficiency of fox-hunting and its enormous expense flew in the face of new economic values.

As a social force resisting agricultural and industrial advances, fox-hunting certainly had a useful role in the countryside for wildlife. Many parts of the country would have had far less woodland had the hunts not planted fox covers, and the kind of landscape that people liked to hunt over was generally much more beneficial to wildlife than arable land.

This remains true today. The hunt countries still exist, though they have been carved up by motorways now. Fox coverts are still cared for and the fox is still valued and encouraged. The top shire packs like the Quorn still hunt several days a week. The Fernie, based in Market Harborough, hunts on Wednesdays and Saturdays, covering a different part of its country at each meet.

They are an extraordinary sight when they leave the village in which they have met, warming themselves with a stirrup cup served from the backs of Landrovers. There is always a following of people in cars who hope to get a view of the chase from a hill top, and one or two others on foot who look out for a fox breaking cover and give a 'whoop' if they see one – which is not very often.

In their red and black coats, the mounted field look like something out of an 18th century reconstruction for a feature film: even their faces seem to look old-fashioned with ruddy cheeks, though few of them are properly farmers. To begin with, the field appears quite orderly as it trots to the first cover in which the hounds look for a fox. The huntsman, in charge of the pack, and his whippers-in, who round up stray hounds, go into the cover while the rest of the field waits outside.

When a fox is seen to break cover, there is a peculiar sense of excitement and confusion. Nobody seems to know which way it has gone, except for a few of the field who gallop off with the hounds. The fox might lead them anywhere and they often disappear from view completely, the only clue as to where they have ended up the distant blowing of horns and singing of the hounds. They might suddenly reappear, miles away, crossing a ploughed field, while the majority of followers are left wandering about rather aimlessly. After an hour or two, the countryside seems to be strewn with stray riders in little groups like the remnants of a defeated army.

When fox-hunting first became really popular in the 18th century, there was a shortage of the animals. In Leicestershire, Meynell took his hounds out of the Quorn territory in 1794 to give the foxes time to recover, and many other hunts had difficulty finding foxes. This was not so much because of the pressure of hunting but because foxes were still regarded by farmers as vermin and were trapped and killed on a large scale. To replenish the supply of foxes, the hunts had to curry favour with farmers and draw them into their social world, at least for the duration of the meet. It was in this way that the hunts began to regard

OVERLEAF *In the heyday of shooting, the gamekeepers had a disastrous effect on the wildlife of the country, and their gibbets were a grim display of their determination to stamp out predators which might take a pheasant, its chicks or its eggs. Thousands of birds of prey were trapped and shot, and many are only now recovering with legal protection.*

themselves as representing some kind of pre-urban egalitarianism in the 19th century, a popular myth which arose out of necessity.

The hunts had to raise money through subscription, and if there were no foxes, income fell off. To keep the customers happy, the practice of bringing in 'bag foxes' arose in the early 19th century, and provided a lively trade in London's Leadenhall Market. The surviving ledgers of one such company, Philip Castang, provide very clear evidence of this trade, which has always been an embarrassment to the hunting fraternity whenever it has retreated to the argument that it is performing a necessary service in pest control in the countryside.

Bagmen became known as Leadenhallers. The Market was the natural place to buy and sell foxes for it also provided much of the hunting gear, saddles and boots, as well as livery stables. The supply of foxes was satisfied in a number of ways. Gamekeepers would take cubs from areas where foxes were plentiful and send them to the market for a good profit, but most probably came from the continent, Holland and France in particular.

There was a great deal of disagreement in hunting circles about the practice of importing foxes and turning down bagmen. Surtees, the great chronicler of fox-hunting in the 19th century, said a bag fox was a 'short running, dastardly traitor, no better nor a 'are (hare)'. French foxes were often frowned upon as 'mongrel-bred vermin ... dodging about like rabbits, their degeneracy ruining the blood of the stout British fox.' They were sometimes called 'French dunghills'.

Despite these criticisms, large numbers of foxes were released – up to fifty pairs in a single season in some parts of the country. All kinds of ruses were employed to put down bag foxes without anybody knowing. The huntsman of the Essex in the period from the 1870s to the 1920s dressed up as a parson, with false beard and whiskers, and kept his foxes hidden at the bottom of his carriage. The turning down of bag foxes was outlawed a long while ago by the Master of Foxhounds Association, but it is no longer necessary anyway for wild foxes are in plentiful supply.

Nobody is quite sure why the fox is doing so well in Britain today. There is no doubt that fox-hunting helped preserve its numbers in the 19th century. It is almost certainly true that foxes, like other predatory animals that had been persecuted by gamekeepers, benefited from the decline in keepering during the two World Wars. It is also said that foxes benefited from myxomatosis, the disease which almost wiped out the rabbit population in Britain. The argument is that the sick rabbits provided foxes with an enormous food supply for a few years and they extended their range. They are now well established in the suburbs of London and other large towns, and it is possible some of these move back into the countryside where they keep the hunts well supplied with sport.

It is characteristic of the story of wildlife in this country that the fox, an animal which has become, in modern times, a symbol of the wild, should have a history so bound up with social and economic change.

Had the fox not been afforded a special status, it would no doubt still have survived for it has a lifestyle which is extremely flexible. It will eat almost anything and it is not confined, like the badger, to particular places in which it sets up home. Foxes roam quite widely and will move their earths readily. They are very agile, can climb high walls and can easily colonize new areas, as their success in town has shown. But it is unlikely foxes would be as common as they are without the influence of fox-hunting and they might well have suffered the same kind of fate as the polecat which was driven out of England in the late 19th century by gamekeepers.

Farmers and gamekeepers did kill foxes in the Victorian period despite the

From the time it became popular in the mid-Victorian period, driven shooting of game – especially pheasant – has had a tremendous influence on the landscape. Vast estates, such as Sandringham, have been layed out with patches of woodland to provide a good day's shoot.

strong social pressures towards preservation. And there was a considerable clash of interests then, as there can be today, between fox-hunting people and those who manage their estates for game. The odd thing is that the fox-hunting dukes were often keen on shooting as well. The landowner had his earth stopper, whose job it was to nurture foxes, as well as his gamekeeper, who would dearly have liked to get rid of foxes altogether. It was said to be not uncommon for a keeper to kill all the foxes he could, but to keep one back and release it in a cover on the day of a hunt. Lacking exercise, the kept fox would be slow and relatively easily caught.

The conflicts between hunting and shooting were fiercest towards the end of the 19th century, when the preservation of game to provide massive bags on the best estates became more and more expensive. These were resolved in many different ways, but quite often the fact that the hunters and the game shooters were of the same class allowed for gentlemanly agreements in which the hunt would take care not to disrupt game, while the preservers would be lenient with the fox.

Killing foxes was not a crime. It was simply frowned upon and there is no record of how many were poisoned or snared. It is probable that the difficulty hunts had in finding foxes, and the reason they began to import them at the turn of the century, was the persecution by gamekeepers and farmers. Whatever the truth of this, the fox certainly seems to have had an easier time of it than many other predators in the English countryside in the Victorian and Edwardian periods.

The shooting of wild birds in the countryside has been popular as long as there have been guns. But 200 years ago, the technology of firepower was not sophisticated enough for birds to be shot easily in flight. Flintlock guns were muzzle loaded – the powder and shot was rammed down the barrel. It took a long time to load up and a long time to reload. A series of innovations from the middle of the 18th century produced a much more efficient shotgun like those used today – shorter double barrels, cartridges which were breech loaded, fired by a percussion cap and containing lead shot which fanned out when it was fired. This gave rise in the 19th century to a completely new kind of shooting which, in turn, affected the landscape as it still does today in counties like Hampshire.

The new sport was driven shooting or the *battue*. In the 18th and early 19th century, shooting generally involved walking through the stubble of the cornfields with dogs and firing at birds on the ground, or as they flew away. One gun would go for the bird on the ground, the other for the one flying off. Grey partridge were the most prized game and they were still abundant where there were cornfields and hedgerows which provided them with food and nesting places and an abundance of insects on which to feed their young among the farmland flowers at the edge of the fields.

Pheasants had been around in Britain at least since Norman times and it is possible some were introduced by the Romans, but they did not commonly breed in the wild until much later. There are many different kinds of pheasant native over a large area of Asia, ranging from the south side of the Caucasus mountains to Japan. They are not unlike chickens and can be kept in a semi-domesticated state, and that is probably how the Norman birds were introduced. These were a variety from the Caucasus mountains, as were most of the introductions in the Middle Ages so that this strain became known as the Old English pheasant. In the 18th century many more were introduced from China. These are the familiar ring-necked pheasant. Other varieties were introduced over the years and they have all now inter-bred, so that those seen pottering around in the fields of Britain today are a mongrel lot.

The Game Laws, which outlawed the shooting of game birds other than by those qualified by status or income, included the pheasant, along with partridge, rabbit and hares from Tudor times. But until the 18th century pheasant were relatively rare in the countryside. It was not until 'driven shooting' got going that the pheasant was really valued and reared in very large numbers to provide sport for the upper classes.

Though game was highly valued and the subject of draconian laws against poaching long before driven shooting came in, this new sport provided a dramatic break with the past. The rapid loading and firing of the shotgun enabled sportsmen to fire almost continuously at birds in the air. With a left and a right, they could bring down two birds in quick succession, and with a second gun and a team of loaders on hand, be ready to have a go at the next two within seconds.

To make full use of this new technology and the skill required to slaughter a great many birds in a short space of time, the *battue* was invented. Prince Albert was a great early exponent of the art and the satirical magazine *Punch* carried a cartoon in 1845 of him blasting away at pheasant, hares and a ragged bundle of

Pheasant shooting remains a popular sport but its effects on the countryside today are often beneficial – a counter to the pressures of intensive farming.

less easily identified beasts while sitting in an armchair in a living room. It is a telling image, for driven shooting quickly became so carefully ordered and controlled that it took the wildness out of the sport, with parties slaughtering hundreds, and even thousands, of birds in a morning, taking an excellent lunch and slaughtering many more in the afternoon.

The driven shoot needs a very large number of birds which have to be especially nurtured and the chicks fed until they are ready to fly. Once the birds have gone semi-wild, every effort has to be made to keep them on the estate that reared them, so they are fed with grain. Anything that might eat the pheasant or its eggs before the day of a shoot has to be slaughtered.

To provide first class sport, an estate had to be landscaped in a particular way. There were woods and covers to provide birds with warmth and protection. Rhododendron bushes were much favoured for this in the 19th century, and this plant, introduced from the Himalayas, is still abundant today on shooting estates. For the shoot itself – which would take place on any one estate only a few times in the winter – everything had to be carefully prepared. The guns were lined up in position, well spaced. Beaters would go into a wood in which the pheasants had been encouraged to congregate and drive the birds out and over the guns. To encourage the birds to fly high, they would be driven over a line of trees. And to encourage them to fly over the guns, a wood was needed behind the firing line which looked to the birds like safety.

OPPOSITE The introduction of pheasants, chiefly from China, has had a profound effect on the countryside. They are still bred in very large numbers for 'driven shooting'. Many varieties are established in the wild. This is an 'Old English' pheasant, one of the earliest introductions from the Caucasus around 900 years ago.

In this way, on the best estates the air would be full of pheasant clattering up into the sky and squawking as the guns blasted away at them. The apotheosis of this kind of shooting came in the Edwardian era, and its greatest exponent was the King himself. As the Prince of Wales, Edward had been handed a prime shooting estate with the purchase of Sandringham in 1861. He set out to improve it, planting woods and coverts and employing an army of keepers who wore bowler hats with gold cords and gold acorns embroidered on the front. Each year, 10,000 pheasant were raised from eggs and a larder was installed which could hold 7,000 birds. Each gun at the Prince's shoots had two or three loaders and, at lunch, the Prince would read out the guests' scores. One of the best shots, Lord Ripon, killed 28 pheasant in one minute and he made the claim that he once had seven dead birds in the air at the same time. There was tremendous rivalry between individuals for the position as the best shot, and between estates for the best bags of any season. In the late Victorian and Edwardian period, shooting became a kind of mania.

In order to sustain it, a larger and larger army of gamekeepers was needed from the middle of the 19th century, not so much to police poachers but to eliminate all predators other than the privileged shooting parties. Pheasant and partridge nest on the ground, and are very vulnerable to foxes, stoats, weasels, polecats and badgers. Even hedgehogs will eat pheasants' eggs. The chicks are eaten by all kinds of birds: magpies, crows, ravens, kestrels, buzzards and so on. The adults will be taken by buzzards, sparrowhawks and the larger birds of prey. Not only that, the appearance of a bird of prey on the day of a shoot is liable to frighten pheasant or partridge away from the woods in which they have been herded in preparation for the beaters.

A hen pheasant, a brightly coloured cock and a red-legged or French partridge 'in the bag'. At one time partridge were the most prized birds for shooting, but they have declined drastically in numbers because of changes in farming practice and use of pesticides and herbicides which has reduced the feed for young birds during the critical first weeks of life.

The heyday of gamekeeping was between the late 1850s and 1914 and this proved to be one of the most destructive periods for wildlife in Britain since the start of the Industrial Revolution. The slaughter of birds of prey and ground predators like the polecat was on an almost unbelievable scale. It was particularly gruesome in Scotland where the vogue for deer stalking and grouse shooting led to an assault on the wildlife at the turn of the century from which some species are only now recovering. Duff Hart-Davies quotes in his book, *Monarchs of the Glen*, the destruction by the keepers at Glengarry in just three years. This included 198 wild cats, 246 pine marten, 106 polecats, 27 white-tailed sea eagles, 15 golden eagles, 46 otters, 462 kestrels, 18 ospreys, 275 kites, 285 common buzzards, 83 hen harriers, 1431 hooded crows, 475 ravens and 371 rough legged buzzards – among others. There was no legal protection for these birds, as there is for many of them now, and a landowner could simply attempt to rearrange the wildlife of an estate as he wished.

At the same time as gamekeepers were attempting to get rid of a great deal of Britain's native wildlife, a Victorian vogue arose for the importation of exotic species from abroad to 'acclimatize' in Britain. Quite a number of plants and animals had been deliberately or accidentally introduced to this country before the 19th century: rabbits, fallow deer, pheasant, rats and mice among them. But the enthusiasm and optimism of the Victorian acclimatizers was unprecedented, and with steam ships to bring back beasts from all over the world, they were better equipped than any previous generation.

Without any concern about the ecological effects of what they did, many landowners released exotic beasts from Africa and Asia, sometimes just out of curiosity to see how they would fare here, to ornament their estates and most often to provide themselves with a richer wildlife to hunt and shoot. Most introductions were failures, such as the elk and moose brought to Woburn by Hastings Duke of Bedford.

One of the greatest enthusiasts for acclimatization in the 19th century was an extraordinary figure called Frank Buckland. He was born in 1826, the son of an eminent geologist, Dean Buckland, and was reputedly weighed as a baby on the kitchen scales against the leg of mutton the family were to have for dinner. Buckland acquired a taste for animals at an early age, and ate anything just to try it – mice and snakes included. He was a serious naturalist, however, and became in time Her Majesty's Inspector of Fisheries. It was Buckland who attempted to bring together the landowners' interest in introducing exotic species into the Society for the Acclimatization of Animals, Birds, Fishes, Insects and Vegetables within the United Kingdom – known as the Acclimatization Society for short.

It held its first meeting in 1860, and was founded in imitation of the Paris Société d'Acclimatation which boasted among its members Napoleon III and the then Pope.

A dinner held in 1859, the same year that Charles Darwin published his *Origin of Species*, provided the scientific and gastronomic inspiration for the Society. Frank Buckland's own account gives a vivid picture of the interests and prejudices of the assembled gathering.

On January 21 1859 I had the good fortune to be invited to a dinner, which will, I trust, hereafter form the date of an epoch in natural history; I mean the now celebrated eland dinner, when, for the first time, the freshly killed haunch of this African antelope was placed on the table of the London Tavern. The savoury smell of the roasted beast seemed to have pervaded the naturalist world, for a goodly

OPPOSITE *A red kite on the carcass of a sheep, with a buzzard waiting its turn. Both these magnificent birds of prey have suffered severely from persecution by gamekeepers and from pesticides and often deliberate poisoning by farmers. The buzzard remains quite common, while the red kite is recovering from near extinction and is still confined to one area of Wales. In Elizabethan times, red kites were common scavengers in London.*

company were assembled, all eager for the experiment. At the head of the table sat Professor Owen himself, his scalpel turned into a carving knife, and his gustatory apparatus in full working order. It was, indeed, a zoological dinner to which each of the four points of the compass had sent its contribution. We had a large pike from the East; American partridges shot but a few days ago in the dense woods of the Transatlantic West; a wild goose, probably a young bean goose, from the North and an eland from the South.

The assembled company were ardent lovers of Nature and all her works: most of them distinguished in their individual departments. The gastronomic trial over, we next enjoyed an intellectual treat in hearing from the professor his satisfaction at having been present at a new epoch in natural history. He put forth the benefits which would accrue to us by naturalizing animals from foreign parts, animals good for food as well as ornamental to the parks.

As it turned out, the acclimatizers were at the end of a zoological era – the Professor referred to was Richard Owen who fiercely opposed Darwin's evolutionary theory, and in doing so, demonstrated his outmoded understanding of the natural world. Most animals could not be uprooted from one continent and successfully released into the wild in Britain – they suffered disease and starvation and died out unless carefully tended. And those that did do well had a tendency to be so successful they were soon branded as pests and attempts were made to wipe them out. The Acclimatization Society lasted only five years and most of the introductions of animals subsequently were made by wealthy men who were also keen naturalists.

The male mandarin duck, a native of China, is now one of the most colourful and exotic breeding birds in England. After several attempts to introduce mandarin ducks in the great age of 'acclimatization' of wildlife abroad, success finally came in the 1930s and these birds are now established around Virginia Water in Surrey.

Two of these stand out as exceptional. One was Edward Rothschild whose family home was at Tring Park, and the other was Hastings Duke of Bedford, who brought many weird and exotic beasts to Woburn, including the herd of Pere David's Deer which still live in the grounds. Between them, these two have been responsible for some of the notable successes at introduction.

One of the most pleasing and colourful of these is the survival in the wild of the mandarin duck. It is an aristocratic looking bird, the male beautifully shaped and brightly coloured like one of those hand painted wooden birds sold in gift shops, the female a much more sober mottled brown. In China these are sacred birds, symbols of love, and they are not hunted. But their native habitat of wooded rivers and lakes has been largely destroyed, and it has been suggested there could be more wild mandarin in England now than in China.

Whether or not that is true, the wild mandarin here are very particular about their habitat, and though attempts have been made to establish them in several parts of the country, they have taken up residence only in the most salubrious places.

The first mandarin were brought over in the 18th century, but there was no serious attempt to get them naturalized until the London Zoo bought two pairs in 1834 for the astronomical price of £35 each. Few imported mandarin had young at first, and it was suggested that the Chinese were caponizing the males – castrating them – to protect their trade. The first record of a mandarin in the wild was one shot in 1866 in Berkshire.

At Woburn, the Duke of Bedford established a breeding colony of mandarins at the end of the 19th century and there were reputedly 300 at the outbreak of the Great War. With its lakes and fine old trees, Woburn was an ideal habitat for the mandarin. These are tree ducks, with a liking for the acorns of parkland oak trees. Old trees provide them with holes for nesting. It seems they rely too, in winter, on the feed put down for pheasant, for the Woburn population plummeted during the Great War when the feeding of birds became illegal due to the national food shortage.

A few Woburn birds ventured beyond Bedfordshire, and turned up in Regents Park before the 1914–18 War. But the biggest wild population now is established in the most salubrious of areas, in Windsor Great Park and around the plush stockbroker homes of Virginia Water. Some of these may have come originally from Woburn but the majority are probably descended from pairs put down by Sir Alfred Ezra on his estate, Foxwarren Park in Surrey in 1928, and another more ambitious attempt to establish them in 1930. Ezra and others imported 99 birds and released them in London, in Buckingham Palace Garden, Hampton Court, and Greenwich and Regents Parks. Nobody is sure what happened to these birds but most flew away, some as far as Hungary and Sweden.

What is certain is that mandarin are quite a common sight now in Windsor Great Park, and Home Park, the private fields and gardens of Her Majesty the Queen at Windsor. They are also on Virginia Water and other lakes in the area which have thickly wooded banks. Mandarin favour the shady lake shores, where they hide themselves sitting on low branches above the water. In spring quite large flocks of 30 or 40 birds can be seen with the males displaying, tossing their heads in a petulant way and chasing the females. Mandarin have been encouraged with nest boxes, which they use quite readily. But one of the most pleasing thoughts is that quite a number have nested in the great oaks of Windsor, planted in the time of Elizabeth I to provide timber for the ships which eventually sailed to China and brought them back.

The mandarin's survival in this Royal parkland is also an indication of the

The little muntjac deer from Asia is one of the most successful introductions of an alien species to Britain. About the size of a small dog, muntjac have spread from the parklands of stately homes to many parts of the Midlands and southern England. They have a special taste for garden roses.

uniqueness of this kind of landscape, which is a survival from the days when much of the countryside was laid out for the pleasure of Kings and Queens and the aristocracy. In the context of modern England, it is a rare and valuable habitat, for the ancient trees, the wood pasture and the lakes have gone from much of the countryside.

Also found in Windsor Great Park, outside the fenced-off enclosure of red deer, is the charming little muntjac deer, quite common though rarely seen for it is shy, and not much larger than a small dog. Muntjac are from Asia, and come in several varieties, most notably Indian and Chinese – these last are called Reeve's muntjac which are smaller than the Indian variety. Again, it was from Woburn at the turn of the century that the first escapees made inroads into the English countryside. There were both Indian and Reeve's muntjac here, and they may have inter-bred. In 1929–31, the Zoological Society released 18 Indian muntjac at Whipsnade, its estate which was made into the famous zoo.

Muntjac in their native habitat live chiefly in long grass and thicket and they do best in England in young woodland with a thick undergrowth. They have spread very quickly throughout the country, and they are still extending their range. In many ways they are ideally suited to the new woodlands of the country, which are left to grow wild, and are not managed intensively as they were in the days before coal replaced wood as a fuel. They are an ideal little beast for the Home Counties and the Midlands, and have a special taste for rose leaves in suburban gardens.

Sooner or later, if they do well, all deer fall foul of foresters and muntjac are beginning to damage trees to an extent which could turn them into a pest species, though so far there has been no attempt to exterminate them. Muntjac are territorial rather than herd animals, living solitary lives most of the time, and the young bucks are driven off to find their own territory when they grow up – a feature of the deer's behaviour which has made its spread quite rapid.

There is another very small deer at large in parts of England which also comes from the 11th Duke of Bedford's collection at Woburn, but has not spread on anything like the same scale so far. This is the Chinese water deer, usually slightly larger than a muntjac. Neither the buck nor the doe has antlers, but the male has small tusks which grow down from the upper jaw. Unlike the muntjac, Chinese water deer are essentially grazing animals, and live on downland as well as in woodland. They are established in parts of Bedfordshire, Buckinghamshire, Hampshire, Northamptonshire, the Norfolk Broads and Shropshire. Their present distribution reflects in whole a series of introductions to estates around the country, from the turn of the century until the mid 1950s. Like muntjac, they are only rarely seen, and not a great deal is known about how well they are doing.

Chinese water deer, though not as numerous as muntjac, have several well-established colonies in southern England.

There is one other Oriental deer well established in parts of Britain from the north of Scotland, down to Dorset. This is the Japanese Sika deer, a much larger beast than muntjac and Chinese water deer, the stag sporting a fine set of antlers. Since their first introduction in the 1860s by the Zoological Society of London in the heyday of acclimatization enthusiasm, three different subspecies brought from Japan, Manchuria and Formosa have gone wild, and as they all inter-breed quite readily, the wild British version is probably something of a mongrel.

Sika are native to densely forested hills on the Japanese islands, and the coastal regions of Siberia. In Britain they have scattered populations around the areas in which they were first introduced. They have not, like muntjac, spread right across the country, though they have made some enterprizing trips. Some brought to Brownsea Island in 1896 immediately swam across Poole Harbour to the Isle of Purbeck in Dorset, and they reputedly still make the trip now and again. The sheer size of Sika will probably limit their scope for expansion in such a heavily populated and cultivated place as Britain, but they will continue to do well locally. There are now plenty of Sika deer on the Ministry of Defence tank firing ranges at Lulworth Cove, and they are well established in much of the new conifer woodland in the Highlands of Scotland. Sika can inter-breed with red deer, so some strange hybrids are possible.

Sika deer are the largest introduced animal to have gone wild in Britain. They, along with muntjac, Chinese water deer, the revived roe deer (see Chapter One) and wild fallow deer which escaped from park herds introduced in Roman times, form a much greater population of deer than existed in the Middle Ages.

The two native species of deer – red and roe – are doing very well, but the larger red are mostly confined to the north of Scotland, to Exmoor, and to the wilder hills in Britain. Britain's deer population is now an odd jumble of species, and conservationists and ecologists are usually unenthusiastic about exotic species which upset the balance of what are regarded as natural communities of native animals. But it is a remarkable thought that there are at large in the woodlands of Britain today greater numbers and a greater variety of deer than when modern industrialism got under way in the mid-18th century. This fact alone at least undermines the popular belief that a kind of Garden of Eden was destroyed by the steam age and that wildlife finds it hard to survive in a landscape cut through with motorways and carved up by giant machines.

A great deal of Britain's wildlife is non-native, and it should be borne in mind that, as an offshore island, the country has a limited range of plants and animals because of an accident of geological and ecological history. At the end of the last Ice Age, around 10,000 years ago, most of Britain was covered in solid ice, and the southern land was a treeless tundra, frozen for most of the year. As the ice retreated, recolonization of plants and animals began from southern Europe and from Asia. But as the ice melted, the sea rose. The land bridge with France was flooded quite early as warmer weather returned and the Channel blocked the advance of many land-bound animals, and some plants. This occurred too with fish, as we saw in Chapter Two. Had this not happened, a range of species might have moved north and gradually reached Britain. It would also have meant that recolonization of species, such as bears and wolves, which became extinct might have been possible from Europe. Islands everywhere have a different, and usually less varied, wildlife than continents.

An extreme example is New Zealand. Before Europeans arrived and brought with them a whole range of birds and mammals, New Zealand had been cut off by the ocean from millions of years of continental evolution. It had, in fact, only one native mammal, a bat, and no land mammals at all so that flightless birds

OPPOSITE *The most unlikely newcomer to the wildlife of Britain – the red necked wallaby, a native of Tasmania. Only two colonies survive in the wild, one in Derbyshire and the other in Sussex. They can be seen most easily at Whipsnade zoo.*

had no predators and such oddities as the kiwi could survive. In New Zealand today there is a fantastic range of species brought in from all over the world. From England there are hedgehogs, stoats, ferrets, weasels, dogs, cats, rats, mice, rabbits, hares, wild cattle, sheep and goats, red deer, fallow deer, wild pigs and wild horses. Among the birds are skylarks, blackbirds, rooks, starlings and house sparrows. From America there are moose, wapiti, Virginia deer and two kinds of quail. From Asia, four kinds of deer, and several birds, and from Australia, wallabies and opossums, and more than half a dozen birds. There are even Maori rats and native dogs from Polynesia.

In comparison, Britain has got off quite lightly. Although their native lands may be a great distance away, in terms of evolutionary history, the naturalized animals in Britain are not that far removed from the indigenous species.

The edible or fat dormouse is wild in the Chiltern Hills near London, having escaped earlier this century from Tring Park, the stately home of Edward Rothschild. It is a close relative of the dormouse which the Romans considered a delicacy and fattened for the table.

One of the most charming, though rarely seen for it is a night-time creature, is the fat dormouse, or – as it is sometimes called – the edible dormouse. This is larger than our native dormouse, about the size of a young grey squirrel, which it resembles. It is creature which might, in time, have made its own way to England from the continent had it not been for the barrier of the Channel, for it is found in most of Europe. Its Latin name is *Glis Glis* and it was a delicacy in the Roman Empire, raised in oak and beech woods, and fed on currants and chestnuts, before it was finally fattened for the table in earthenware pots.

Another much more successful introduction which can also be eaten is the now very common grey squirrel. It is native to North America and was brought in several times during the 19th century, before a group of ten was let loose at Woburn in 1890 and rapidly multiplied. There were many other introductions up to the 1930s when the grey squirrel had spread all over southern England and the Midlands and had become a pest. In 1937, the further importation of greys was prohibited and attempts were made to exterminate it, but it was much too late. The greys had taken over the territory left by the ailing native red squirrel population which had declined since the turn of the century due to disease. Greys are larger than red squirrels and appear to be much happier in broad-leafed woodland. Red squirrels are now generally confined to pine forests in Britain, while the greys are much more widely distributed, such a familiar sight in parks and suburban gardens that they are regarded as solidly British by most people, who would no doubt be horrified to discover in the great American culinary work *The Joy of Cooking* an illustration of how to skin them and prepare them for the pot.

Exactly why grey squirrels were brought over from America is unclear; it seems there was simply the idea that they would look pretty in our parks. There is no possibility now of getting rid of them, though their numbers are still kept down by foresters and park keepers who surreptitiously cull them in the early morning to avoid public anger at the slaughter of such endearing little animals.

The list of successful introductions is much longer than has been given here, but the above examples are among the most significant and serve to show the extent to which the wildlife of Britain has been influenced by the attitudes of those who have taken pleasure from using the countryside as their own personal playground.

A greater understanding of ecology and the balance of nature has put an end to such experimentation and new introductions have all been accidental or due to natural causes. An example of the latter is the astonishing spread of the collared dove through Europe from its original home in Syria. Collared doves look like slim pigeons and make a rather unpleasant rasping noise.

Something happened to them genetically which enabled them to extend their range and since the last war they have spread to many parts of Britain, though not into the big towns where the feral pigeon and woodpigeon appear to have kept them at bay. Insects and wild plants continue to turn up in consignments of food and in ships and keep the pest controllers busy, but the great age of acclimatization is otherwise over.

The hunting and shooting interests are much more concerned now with maintaining the stocks of birds and mammals which are native or established here and, in doing so, have found themselves in conflict with farmers who, since the 1930s, have been armed with far more devastating weapons than traps and guns. The rise of the chemical industry and the development of much more powerful pesticides and herbicides has laid the ground for the most serious conflict in the countryside since the start of industrialism.

OPPOSITE *Britain's native red squirrel with characteristic ear tufts. It has been replaced in many parts of the country by the larger grey squirrel brought in from North America around the turn of the century.*

In this context, the fate of the little grey partridge is telling, for its rise and decline involves many of the changes that have affected the countryside in the past 100 years. Despite the fact that the native stock of grey partridge has often been topped up with birds from the continent, and the red-legged partridge or Frenchman has been successfully introduced here, these little game birds are not doing well and have been declining since the turn of the century.

They thrive in rich countryside of cornfields and hedgerows, and for centuries their numbers must have been high. Traditionally they were shot in the stubble of the cornfields after the harvest. New farming methods began to undermine

the habitat of the partridge, and though it was a favourite bird among the shooting fraternity and many were bred and 'turned down' on estates, it went into a sharp decline. The rotation of crops and corn cut with a scythe leaving a long stubble for the partridge were replaced by artificially fertilised farmland and close-cut corn. This was the chief reason for the fall in partridge numbers.

Imperial Chemical Industries, a major manufacturer of shotgun cartridges in the 1930s, was worried about the decline of the partridge as it would affect trade. It set up a research project which, in time, became the Game Conservancy, based at Fordingbridge in Hampshire, to investigate the problem and to see what could be done. Recent investigations revealed that one critical problem for partridge was that the insect life on which their young depended for a rich protein diet during the first weeks of life had been wiped out by herbicides which killed off the plants on which the insects live. By leaving the edge of fields unsprayed, partridge did better – though never as well as in the days of less intensive agriculture. ICI, once a producer of shotgun cartridges, is, of course, a producer of chemical sprays so that, in time, one side of its business affected another. It is characteristic of the pervasiveness of the chemical industry in modern life and the complexity of its effects on the landscape and ecology of Britain. And it is to this that we move on in the next chapter.

5 Chemical Reactions

As twilight dims the Tees estuary and thousands of workers set off inland for home, a coach presses in the opposite direction along the flat, windswept service roads. It is taking tourists to see Teesside's latest attraction: the dazzling illuminations of ICI, which light up the night sky for miles around. They come to marvel at the monstrous shining structures of the nation's fourth largest industry, source of raw materials for practically every other modern industrial activity. The tours are organized by the Tees Development Corporation, who are promoting the estuary as Europe's premier site for the chemical industry. A number of the world's major chemical companies have production plants here, among them BASF, Tioxide, Philips and, of course, ICI, who employ 15,000 people on three separate sites in the estuary.

As dawn approaches and the day shift begins to make its way back to work, the estuary's more permanent residents are also about. Short-eared owls quarter the ground, low over the scrub, hunting for voles. Larks flit across the rough grass then soar high, higher than the tallest steel stack, further than the eye can see. And literally thousands of wading birds, more than 30 different species, descend on Seal Sands to feed on the rich pickings of the mudflats.

Noticeboards tell you particular areas are designated nature reserves: Cowpen Marsh, on lease from ICI to the Cleveland Trust for Nature Conservation, is covered with mallard, teal and widgeon. Shoveler and pintail often visit too. Aquatic plants such as sea sperries, sea lavender and sea milkwort have taken root in the brinefields, which can be twice as salty as the sea in patches. A sign says a series of ponds nearby is called Saltholme Pools. They were formed when the ground subsided after the underlying brine had been pumped out at the turn of the century. They are thick with widgeon and lapwing – another conservation area. Just west of these pools, east of the sea wall known as the Long Drag, is a natural reedbed formed in an area of standing water, another legacy of early brining. The bed is rich in birdlife, home to reed warblers.

A shelduck emerges from a crevice in the slag where it has made its nest and heads for Dormans Pool, where it will feast on the larvae left by flies to hatch in the brackish water. Grey partridge are frequent visitors to the pools too. A long figure, wrapped against the cold North wind and laden with pairs of binoculars, stops to ask if you have spotted the latest rare visitor to the estuary. He has heard reports of one sighted and he believes several hundred more 'twitchers' – fanatical bird spotters – are on their way. Bursts of colour from the many wild flowers which have colonized the estuary break up the scrubby green. Marsh and spotted orchids, yellow-wort, Hare's foot clover and Blue Fleabane, all lime-loving plants, have been attracted to the estuary by the alkaline slag, dumped to reclaim the mudflats.

It is one of the mysteries of the estuary that, despite the massive programme of reclamation dating back two centuries, the number of wading birds using it as a winter feeding ground has actually increased. Teesmouth is an internationally important site for overwintering birds, which cram into a tenth of the mudflat area once available to them.

OPPOSITE *A scene which illustrates the extraordinary complexity and chemistry of the natural world. Adult reed warblers feed a cuckoo chick they have raised in their nest woven on to the stems of Norfolk Reed. Reed warblers are programmed to accept the giant changeling chick – the reeds have a special quality which allows them to grow in and detoxify polluted mud.*

The first moves to reclaim the estuary came in 1740 with the building of a sea wall along the northern edge to restrict tidal flooding of grazing marsh. Then the land-hungry iron and steel industries, ate up nearly half the mudflats – a thousand out of the 2,400 hectares – in the 1890s, using slag from their own blast furnaces. The oil and chemical industries, relative newcomers to the estuary, have now taken back 75 per cent of the remainder, the bulk during the fifties, sixties and early seventies.

It is a bleak and apparently inhospitable landscape but as with so many industrial areas which, like ICI's Wilton Works, take up only a third of their available land area, vast expanses of some classic semi-natural habitats remain undisturbed, a haven for all manner of wildlife.

It goes against the grain to think of an international centre for the chemical industry as set in a nature reserve. For it is undoubtedly the rise of the modern chemical industry which has posed the greatest threat to wildlife and the environment since industrialism began.

From the outset, the chemical industry was a major polluter of the environment. In its early days, at the beginning of the 19th century, the chemical industry was not much more than a trade in one group of chemicals only – the alkalis. Alkali substances neutralize acids. As soda ash and caustic soda, they were essential to a range of 19th century industries including soap, glass and textiles. Demand for alkalis grew steadily and the trade kept pace with its clients' expansion largely by developing more efficient production processes.

Until the 1820s, nearly all the alkalis supplied came from Spanish imports of ash from the barilla plant. Then an ingenious new process, named after its inventor, Nicolas LeBlanc, changed all that and made Britain self-sufficient. LeBlanc perfected the first viable commercial process for synthesising soda from salt using sulphuric acid, coal and limestone.

But soda ash was not all that was produced. Along with it came a black and foul-smelling mass of calcium sulphide and unreacted limestone and coal. Hundreds of thousands of tons of these waste slurries were simply dumped on the industry's own doorstep, in lagoons or 'lime beds' around the alkali works.

By the 1880s a new method called the Solvay process, also named after its inventor, this time a Belgian, had been invented and was taking over. Solvay made soda production beautifully simple: he just let carbon dioxide react with a concentrated solution of salt saturated with ammonia. But this process too produced a pungent waste slurry which was dealt with in much the same manner as before.

Much of the sulphuric acid produced in the first stage of the LeBlanc process went on to be heated with salt and manganese oxide to make chlorine for the textile industry. But vast quantities of hydrochloric acid also resulted and were pumped into the atmosphere. The burning of low-grade coal to heat the salt pans added to the poisonous cocktail. Farmers and landowners for miles around cried out for compensation for the damage done to their crops and woodlands.

It was the alkali trade which prompted one of the first modern State attempts to control pollution. The Alkali Acts of 1863 and 1874, backed up by the Alkali Inspectorate, were unlike other factory acts of the period in that they were concerned not so much for the health of those working in the factory as for all those living around it. The first act enforced condensation of 95 per cent of the hydrochloric acid from the salt furnaces. Large sums were paid out in compensation.

One of the first great studies of pollution also dates from this time. A scientist called Angus Smith, who was one of the first alkali inspectors, published his research in a volume entitled *Air and Rain* in 1872. In it he drew attention to the damage done by acid rain crystals.

Such legislation finally put a stop to the worst of the chemical pollution around the salt towns of Cheshire. Now, a hundred years later, the smog and acid clouds have gone. The chemical works are still there though, much bigger and more sophisticated than ever before. But the land around them, where once the evil-smelling wastes were dumped, is transformed. Hundreds of purple orchids, northern and southern marsh orchids, fragrant orchids, spotted orchids and marsh helleborine are growing in the alkaline soils. More akin to the chalk downlands of the south, the lime beds, now settled and dried out, support a rich variety of wild flowers. Botanically, they have become very important as a text-book illustration of colonization from scratch. The lime beds had no organic content at all; on the contrary they were highly toxic.

Around 20 million cubic feet of waste slurries were dumped in the Witton limebeds over a 40 year period. They were full by 1935. The first signs of vegetation began to appear during the 1950s. Now the beds have been designated an area of special scientific interest and are the subject of a rescue operation launched to save them from being swamped by an adjacent rubbish tip. The Solvay process is still in use today and waste slurries are still dumped in lagoons around the works. Most of the processes involved in the production of chemicals for industry are now, however, light years ahead of those employed by the 19th century alkali manufacturers.

During the first decade of the 20th century scientists made tremendous breakthroughs in organic chemistry, inventing new materials and replacing the natural sources for others. Nineteenth century scientists had gone some way towards relieving the pressure on natural sources of raw materials such as rubber but their inventions were only semi-synthetic chemically modified forms of the original material. Developments from 1910 onwards were wholly synthetic, truly new materials. Yet it took two world wars to bring them to any commercial significance.

The wars and competition from abroad, notably Germany, hastened technological development by shifting the emphasis from the small independent inventor to the large research team backed by government or major corporation. One by one each new development spawned a whole industry of its own.

Four new wholly synthetic materials were already being made in this country on the eve of the Second World War: nylon, polyethylene, polyvinyl chloride (PVC) and polystyrene. During the war years these became large tonnage plastics. Nylon, for instance, was discovered in 1938 and aimed at the women's stocking market but war gave it the opportunity to demonstrate its versatility in such things as parachute cord. Wartime shortages of natural materials such as rubber and fats for detergent production accelerated the development in Germany of synthetic substitutes.

The rise of the plastics industry in this country immediately after the Second World War sparked off another revolutionary change in the chemical industry: the shift from coal to petroleum as the source of organic – carbon-based – raw materials. British firms were the first in Europe to use petroleum as a source of chemical production. Immediately after the war, the large petroleum companies established refineries in the UK and some of the larger chemical manufacturers installed plants nearby. ICI were among the first with their petrochemical plant, Wilton, next to Philips' refinery in the Tees estuary. Along with natural gas, crude oil is now the raw material for over 90 per cent by weight of world production of organic chemicals.

OVERLEAF *Oblivious to the dangers of the modern chemical industry, thousands of starlings fly into their winter roost among the factories on the Tees estuary. They are probably attracted by the warmth.*

Among the new industries to develop under the impetus of wartime pressures was one which now accounts for 3 per cent of the output of the chemical industry – agrochemicals.

Before the war, the only pesticides in common use were simple inorganic chemicals such as arsenate of lead, zinc or copper, or plant derivatives such as pyrethrum from chrysanthemum flowers or rotenone from derris root. Farmers spotted the value of pest control as far back as the late 18th century. The chemical approach began in the 1760s with the use of poisonous plant compounds such as those mentioned above. Biological controls started around the same time with the importation of the Indian mynah bird into Mauritius to control the red locust. The modern era of this approach started in 1888 with the importation of the vedalia beetle into California to control cotton-cushiony scale.

The only important synthetic organic chemical in use before the Second World War was dinitro-ortho-cresol (DNOC), which was introduced as a weed killer in 1932. During the war, labour shortages prompted the use of synthetic plant growth regulators which had been independently discovered in Britain and the United States. MPCA and 2,4,-5 were first used in Britain by the highway authority at Gloucestershire County Council to control plant growth on roadside verges.

Perhaps the best known pesticide of all, DDT, also owes its success, or notoriety, to the Second World War. The chemical, a complex synthetic organic molecule of hydrogen, chlorine and carbon, properly called dichlorodiphenyltrichloroethane, was first synthesized by a German in 1874. However, no use had ever been found for it. Then a Swiss scientist, Dr Paul Muller, working for J.R. Geigy AG, discovered the chemical had powerful insecticidal properties. The company had been manufacturing a moth proofing agent called Mitin FF for many years and was hoping to develop agents effective against a wider range of pests. The Geigy board were astonished by Muller's findings. In 1942 they informed the British and American legations in Switzerland, who seized upon the discovery at once.

The Japanese had just invaded Malaya and cut the Allies off from supplies of derris root. Millions had died during the First World War of insect-borne diseases and both British and Americans were alert to the dangers. DDT was immediately tested as an agent against body lice. Volunteers spent weeks wearing underclothes impregnated with the chemical. Lice on them died at once and they remained uninfested for weeks afterwards as a result of the one application. No-one showed any symptoms of poisoning. It was this combination of such unprecedented persistence and low toxicity to humans which made DDT so successful. The new chemical was hailed as a godsend. It was to save Naples from a typhus epidemic and relieved untold suffering in the tropics, where as little as one pound per acre effectively freed even the swamps from malaria-bearing mosquitoes.

Muller received the Nobel Prize and his work led to the development after the war of even more potent organochlorine insecticides including BHC, lindane and the cyclodiene family of dieldrin, aldrin and endrin. More wartime research, this time by a German, Gerhard Schrader, also led to the discovery of more powerful insecticides, the organophosphorous compounds, built on a hydrogen, carbon and phosphate molecule. Schrader's discovery was no coincidence. He was working on poison gases and insects were widely used to test for potential chemical weapons.

When war ended in 1945, military stockpiles of DDT and the equipment with which to apply it came on to the market in a flood. It quickly found use in the home, the garden, on pets and, of course, in farming.

Military stockpiles of nitrates after the First World War had already spurred on developments in the manufacture of synthetic fertilizers. Phosphates derived from bombs, flares, shells and incendiary rounds also went into the land.

Along with the mechanization and advances in genetics, the new chemical technologies revolutionized farming. Productivity and efficiency have increased steadily to the point where today the UK is 80 per cent self-sufficient in temperate foods. Food production increased by 50 per cent in the first 20 years after the war alone. Farming became agribusiness.

Post-war demand for more food of better quality stimulated the growth of the pesticide industry. The number of approved products shot from 63 in 1944 to more than 800 in 1976. Today there are more than 4,000, although this figure does reflect the variety of formulations available of each product.

The synthetic organic insecticides were so efficient that other means of pest control fell into neglect. During the 1950s the introduction of powerful 'autoblast' machines and aerial crop spraying provided a more powerful means to apply chemical weaponry.

It is difficult to convey the optimism of the late 1940s and early 1950s, knowing what we do now about the effects of DDT and the other organochlorines on the environment. DDT has only the same toxicity as aspirin, which is not to say that it is not poisonous – just as an overdose of aspirin can kill, so did over-use of DDT. But DDT was effective not just because it could kill insects without apparently harming man and other animals but because it remained potent for such a long time before breaking down.

The other organochlorines work in much the same way but are even more potent and persistent. All the cyclodiene family – aldrin, dieldrin and endrin – have been shown to be many times more toxic than DDT, with endrin the most poisonous of all, fifteen times as poisonous to mammals, thirty times as poisonous to fish and 300 times as poisonous to birds. Furthermore, instead of breaking down eventually to give more or less inert substances, the 'drins transformed in the soil or in living tissues to equally or even more toxic chemicals. Aldrin itself, for instance, disappears relatively quickly but was soon discovered to have transformed itself into dieldrin, which lasted unchanged in the soil and in living mammals for as much as another ten years. Another organochlorine, heptachlor, was discovered to be transforming itself into heptachlor epoxide, considerably more poisonous than heptachlor itself.

It is the persistence of the organochlorines which makes them such a threat to wildlife. They are chemically very stable. Although practically insoluble in water, they are soluble in fat. This means they can be stored in the fatty tissues of animals and birds which may eat them or something which has eaten them. And it is when these chemicals become associated with food chains that they do the most damage.

All the organochlorines are biologically very potent. They do not just poison an organism, they enter and distort its biological processes, destroying the enzymes the body needs to protect it from harm, blocking processes which should produce energy. They strike at the central nervous system and cause severe liver damage. And because they take so long to break down, they build up in animals to dangerous levels and either kill them outright or severely affect their breeding.

By the mid-1950s it was becoming clear that all was not well. Large numbers of birds and foxes were reported to be dying in mysterious circumstances. The dream was beginning to turn sour. The first deaths were noticed in the spring of 1956. Five hundred wood pigeons were found dead under one roost; there were reports of pigeons dropping dead mid-flight and heavy casualties among pheasant and partridge. In one 1,500 acre area of Lincolnshire woodland alone 5,668 wood pigeons, 118 stock doves, 59 rooks, 89 pheasants, 16 partridges, 14 long-eared owls, 5 sparrowhawks and 2 racing pigeons were found dead. The victims were mainly seed-eating birds but hawks and other predators such as foxes were also affected.

The British Trust for Ornithology and the Royal Society for the Protection of Birds, along with the Nature Conservancy, the Game Research Association and the Ministry of Agriculture, were all alerted and began to monitor the situation. It was not long before circumstantial evidence enabled them to piece together what was happening and to point the finger at the new organochlorine pesticides. The deaths all occurred in eastern England, where wheat and other cereals are grown: they happened in the spring, always just after sowing.

Seeds had been successfully treated for years with mercury fungicides without side-effects. When aldrin and dieldrin became widely available in the mid-1950s, their effectiveness made them ideal candidates for seed-dressings. They were used chiefly to protect wheat against soil pests such as wheat bulb fly and wireworm. The smallest amounts were used; three ounces was enough for an acre. And it protected the young wheat plant well. But birds dug up the grain and ate it. Their corpses remained toxic and predatory birds and foxes higher up the food chain were poisoned too.

In January and February 1960, 1,300 foxes were found dead. Others were seen wandering around, obviously sick. One even blundered into the yard of a Master of the Hunt. They appeared to be suffering from a virus, dying in a few hours in convulsions and apparent blindness. Public concern mounted. The hunts were particularly worried. Fitzwilliam country, Northamptonshire, was largely denuded of foxes. The Nature Conservancy and the Master of Fox Hounds Association investigated and gradually the connection was made. The Laboratory of the Government Chemist finally succeeded in perfecting tests for detecting dieldrin and post mortem analyses revealed heavy concentrations in some corpses.

In 1962, a voluntary ban on seed dressings containing aldrin, dieldrin and heptachlor was announced and bird deaths declined dramatically.

Some thought the pesticides problem had come to an end but scientists knew they were only just beginning to understand how big the problem was. Perhaps the most valuable lessons were learned from the case of the peregrine falcon, which was brought to the verge of extinction by dieldrin and DDT.

The peregrine is the largest of the breeding falcons in Britain. The female is considerably bigger than the male but both sexes appear similar otherwise. The peregrine feed almost exclusively on birds, especially pigeons. It makes its kill in the air, diving swiftly in a stoop of up to 150 mph. Peregrines nest on cliffs or crags or in quarries. The nest, or eyrie, is simply a scrape on a cliff ledge. The peregrine usually lays three or four eggs, at two-day intervals. Most of the incubation is done by the female, who is brought food by the male. He also brings food for the young when they are first hatched, while she remains at the nest. The young stay in the nest for five or six weeks before venturing out on their own but continue to be fed for some time afterwards. Peregrine chicks mature in their second year and may then start to breed. They live for up to 10 years.

OPPOSITE *The peregrine falcon was a victim of pesticide poisoning in the years just after the war. Years of scientific detective work revealed what was killing it, and the banning of DDT and other pesticides has saved it so that it is common again now, hunting along the seashores in winter.*

If ever a bird symbolized the effect man can have on wildlife, it is the peregrine falcon. During the Middle Ages, the peregrine was prized by kings and noblemen for its hunting skill and killing power. The bird was greatly admired and often figured in portraits, engravings, tapestries and carvings. Interference with it brought harsh penalties. But the invention of gunpowder and development of

A snipe feeding on estuary mud. These and other wading birds which migrate between nesting grounds and winter refuges rely on estuaries for refuelling and are threatened by the colonisation of these areas by modern industry.

the shotgun brought a new kind of sport and the peregrine's fortunes plummeted. Game shooting became the fashionable pursuit and war was declared on predators. Throughout the 19th century, gamekeepers persecuted the peregrine mercilessly. Between 1837 and 1840, 98 peregrines were slaughtered on one Inverness-shire estate alone.

As gamekeeping declined after the First World War the peregrine began to recover, only to face more hostility from devotees of another new sport: pigeon racing. The development of the railways helped this sport to popularity, providing the most convenient means of transporting homers to their release points miles away. The peregrines' fondness for domestic pigeon made it no friends amongst the fanciers, who began a long campaign against them. Victory for the fanciers came during the Second World War when carrier pigeons were enlisted to carry military messages. They proved a lifeline to airmen who crash-landed while on sea patrol around the north-eastern and western coasts. The pigeons would travel with the airmen and be released with details of their location. To protect the carrier pigeons in their line of duty, wartime emergency defence regulations provided for the destruction of peregrine falcons in certain areas of Britain. The order was taken as *carte blanche* for the whole country, especially in the south-east, an area not specified in the emergency regulations. In all, something like 600 birds were killed between 1940 and 1945, and many nests were destroyed.

The wartime order expired in 1946 and the peregrine's status returned once more to the limited protection afforded under the Wild Birds Protection Acts of the 1890s. The new Protection of Birds Act 1954 marked an era of much greater concern for wildlife in Britain. It afforded the peregrine total protection and numbers seemed to be recovering. But during the late 1950s the pigeon fanciers' hostility to the peregrine surfaced again. Enormous numbers of homers were being killed, they claimed, and peregrines were to blame. The fanciers complained to the Home Office and petitioned to have the falcon's legal protection removed. The Home Office was in a difficult position. Wanting to be sure of their facts, they commissioned a survey by the The British Trust for Ornithology (BTO) through the Nature Conservancy Council. The enquiry was launched late in 1960 along with a nationwide appeal for information.

Earlier reports of declines in population in the south of England and Wales did not square with the pigeon fanciers' claims. By the end of the first year of the enquiry, it was clear that concern was appropriate not so much for the pigeon as for the peregrine, which was plunging into a headlong decline.

Widespread poisoning of birds and foxes by newly introduced seed dressings drew the enquiry's attention to pesticides as a possible factor in the decline. The search for evidence began. A peregrine egg from Perthshire was analyzed and found to contain not just dieldrin, but DDE – the breakdown product of DDT – heptachlor epoxide and gamma BHC. The chemicals were present in too small amount to kill but their presence proved a peregrine living in hill country miles from any arable land could accumulate a variety of pesticide residues through feeding on contaminated prey. It gave some measure of the extent of contamination of the environment by pesticides.

The pattern of decline across the country, strongest in arable areas, and the timing – from 1956 onwards – both matched up with the introduction of the more potent organochlorine insecticides. But, disturbingly, while bird deaths in general were considerably fewer after the introduction of a voluntary ban on seed dressings in 1962, the peregrine continued to decline. Monitoring and analysis of corpses and eggs went on until the organizer of the enquiry, Derek Ratcliffe, began to investigate something which had puzzled him for years. Ratcliffe had always been fascinated by the peregrine and had examined many eyries before any problems were apparent. Before 1950 he had come across only one broken egg. In 1951, five out of nine eyries he examined contained broken eggshells. Then he saw a female eating one of her own eggs. Similar scenes were witnessed by others in subsequent years and many more incidents were recorded. Clearly, if widespread, this would have a significant effect on the population. Ratcliffe was determined to see if this was at the root of the peregrine's decline.

The egg-breaking phenomenon could not be the result of the same pesticides used in the new seed dressings, for it pre-dated their introduction by several years. Exactly how many years Ratcliffe began to work out with the help of the Natural History Museum and some less official egg collectors. By careful weighing and measuring, Ratcliffe deduced that from 1947, peregrine eggshells were significantly thinner and more prone to break. Other birds of prey such as sparrowhawks, merlins and kestrels seemed to be suffering too, though not to the same extent as the peregrine. Ratcliffe had long suspected that one of the less toxic organochlorines might be responsible. Neither DDT nor gamma BHC was included in the voluntary ban. As early as March 1946, the *Racing Pigeon* magazine carried an advertisement for a DDT dust suitable for controlling ectoparasites on homing birds. The potential for contamination of peregrines was enormous. Proof came when a homing pigeon ring found in an eyrie in 1947 was analyzed. Both DDT and its breakdown product DDE were found.

The discovery came in the nick of time, for the peregrine in this country was on the verge of extinction. The fate of the peregrine brought home just how dangerous the new pesticides could be, how insidiously they worked in the environment. Study upon study was launched to research the effects. Traces of DDT were found to have spread throughout the world – even penguins in the Antarctic were said to contain residues. No-one did more to warn of the dangers than Rachel Carson in her book *Silent Spring* published in 1962. DDT became a symbol of pollution. It was eventually banned in 1984 but traces of it will be with us for a long time to come. Analysis of peregrines' eggs laid between 1948 and 1952 still contained DDE more than 30 years later.

Dieldrin was banned finally only last year (1989) although its use in sheep dips and seed dressings was restricted in 1975. But vast quantities remain in the environment and are even today wreaking havoc with our wildlife. The otter is now known to have fallen victim.

The otter is such a secretive animal that very little is known about its behaviour and ecology. One thing is certain, however, they have become increasingly scarce and since 1978 have been regarded as an endangered species. One of the largest carnivores in Britain, the otter is only slightly smaller than a badger but, unlike the badger, otters are found only near water and well away from people. The decline in their numbers began in the late 1950s and has been shown to reflect precisely the use of dieldrin. Otters all but disappeared from the southern and eastern counties of England, the cereal-growing areas where use of seed dressings was highest, and from the north-west, where dieldrin was widely used in sheep dips. The story was the same: dieldrin drained off the land into the rivers and streams and was absorbed by fish. The otters fed on the fish and especially eels, which were found to contain massive concentrations of the pesticide. Residues built up in the otters, sometimes killing them outright, often severely affecting their breeding. Threats to their habitat from anglers and other water sports enthusiasts have compounded the otter's problems.

Both dieldrin and DDT residues have been found in the bodies of the thousands of common seals which died around our coasts early in 1989. Scientists are unsure

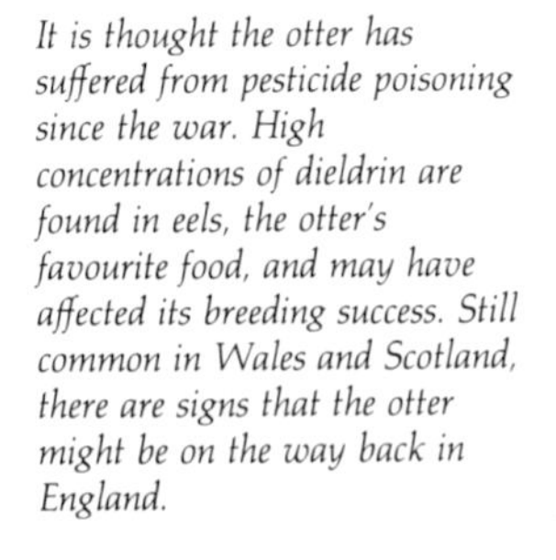

It is thought the otter has suffered from pesticide poisoning since the war. High concentrations of dieldrin are found in eels, the otter's favourite food, and may have affected its breeding success. Still common in Wales and Scotland, there are signs that the otter might be on the way back in England.

what part, if any, the organochlorines may have played in the deaths. Research has now ruled out direct poisoning but it has been suggested that organochlorines and a group of industrial chemicals of a similar structure called polychlorinated biphenyls (PCBs) may have lowered the seals' resistance to a virus.

Today the peregrine is one of this country's great conservation success stories. It is back in even greater numbers, doing better than ever before. But it took a great deal of care and action on the part of voluntary organizations and the public. The RSPB today have two public hides specially designed for people to watch this stunning bird: one in Yorkshire and one in Gloucestershire. Last year, 13,000 made the trip to Rishworth in Yorkshire specifically to see the peregrines, and 100,000 tourists combined taking in views over the Wye Valley with a look at the peregrines at Simmonds Yat.

Since the 1960s, our understanding of the ecology of the natural world has come on in leaps and bounds. We have new respect for our wildlife, not least as an indicator of trouble in our environment. For if ever a creature brought home to man the danger of what he was doing to the environment, it was the peregrine falcon. We are far more cautious now about what we pump into the environment. Research and development of a new pesticide now accounts for 60 per cent of the cost of launching a new product and takes around 7 years.

The fears of pollution aroused by the pesticide scandal and the knowledge of what chemicals, both agricultural and industrial, can do to the environment boosted ecological research tremendously. The heavy concentration of industry, particularly chemical works, in the Tees estuary prompted investigations by Durham University.

For twenty years now, a team of zoologists have been monitoring the health and behaviour of shore birds visiting the Tees estuary. At regular intervals during the winter season, the team lie in wait for the birds on the spit by Seal Sands. As the tide begins to rise, thousands of dunlin, oystercatchers, shelduck and ringed plovers, among others, descend cutting a swirling pattern in the sky. The mudflats come alive as they pick hungrily at the vast numbers of worms and snails, up to two million per square metre. As the tide rushes in, the birds have their fill and then roost in the space remaining. Suddenly, an almighty blast rips through the calm. Three cannon nets are sent flying through the air, engulfing the birds as they sleep off their meal. A split second later, the mudflats are alive again, this time with students from the university who come hurtling down the spit with boxes and begin to disentangle their captive birds ready for study and ringing.

Once all have been accounted for, the students settle in a circle on the spit with their clipboards to take the visitors' particulars. 'This little chap's been here before. He's wearing one of our rings already. He's a dunlin, originally from Siberia, now on his way back. And he must be a good 20 years old' the professor tells them. A student gently blows back the Russian dunlin's breast feathers to see how much fat it has stored away for the long trip home – it might fly as much as 2,000 miles at a stretch. The bird is weighed and measured and then released. One found dead along the shoreline, well away from the nets, is taken back to the laboratory for dissection.

One of the team's main interests has been the effects of heavy metals such as cadmium, mercury, zinc and lead on the shore birds and the estuarine environment in general. Much to their surprise, both monitoring and analysis of dead birds have shown they are unharmed. Over 99 per cent of cadmium, mercury, zinc and lead taken up by the birds in their food and water passes straight through them. The cadmium, however, remains in the birds tissues. Some of the tiny amount of mercury stored by the birds during late winter ends up lodged in the feathers

OPPOSITE *There are huge colonies of seabirds, puffins, kittiwakes, guillemots and auks on the Isle of May in the Firth of Forth. A remarkable piece of research has revealed that some, like the puffin, have a kind of natural immunity to some toxic metals.*

and is then moulted before the breeding season. This last finding in particular has enabled scientists to follow the fate of metals within one estuary and its dumping in moulted feathers miles away on another estuary.

Meanwhile, further north in the heavily industrialized Firth of Forth, scientists have been studying the effects of heavy metals on seabirds living on the Isle of May. Oil pollution from the refinery at Grangemouth; run-off from mines and TBT anti-fouling paint used by fishermen and yachtsmen; sewage sludge and distillery effluent; all combine to make the estuary an apparently hazardous place for wildlife. Yet the Firth of Forth continues to be an internationally important estuary for seabirds and has no fewer than fourteen Sites of Special Scientific Interest.

The furthest island out to sea, the Isle of May, lies for much of the year shrouded in dense fog. The rocky coastline makes it hard to land. Boats stopping for any length of time must anchor off-shore. Few trees grow here, the soil is so thin. Over much of the island the greenstone rock of which the May is entirely composed lies bare.

During the Middle Ages monks set up a priory on the May; more recently the human inhabitants have been the lighthouse keepers and their families. Today, however, the lighthouse is fully automated and the island has been returned to the birds. The Isle of May has been as a bird sanctuary since 1956. Then there were only about half a dozen puffins on the island. Now there are more than 40,000. The colourful red and blue billed birds bob up and down in the menacing swell of the sea and gather in clans among the sea campion around their deep breeding burrows, which honeycomb the island.

To check what seabirds living miles from industry might absorb the scientists chose a colony living on the cleanest, least polluted island they could think of. The tiny island of St Kilda in the Outer Hebrides lies in the north-east Atlantic. Abandoned by its few inhabitants in 1930, the only humans there now are the people who run an Army radar station. First and foremost, St Kilda is home to half a million puffins, as well as fulmars, kittiwakes, gannets and a host of others.

Like the peregrine, the puffins' fortunes have risen and fallen with man's own. For hundreds of years, the St Kildans scratched a living on their inhospitable island. Cut off from the mainland for many months of the year by stormy seas,

RIGHT *The fulmar, along with the puffin, has featured in studies of the effects of toxic metals on seabirds. During this century fulmars have had a spectacular increase in numbers and have spread from the islands of St Kilda to many parts of the mainland coast.*

OVERLEAF *A comparison of puffins living miles out in the Atlantic on the islands of St Kilda and those on the Isle of May showed that the more remote colony had a higher concentration of some toxic metals in their bodies. It is now thought the origin of these poisons is often natural, not industrial.*

they relied on the seabirds for food. They took their feathers for down and used the oil too. Vast numbers of birds were harvested: one visitor estimated the 180 islanders living on St Kilda in 1697 took 16,000 eggs a week along with 22,600 birds. So great was the islanders' dependency on the seabirds that they were excluded from the provisions of the Preservation of Seabirds Act 1869. Catching the birds was quite an art. The islanders defied rocky heights and sheer drops to lay ingenious little nooses to trap the birds by their feet. Julian Huxley nicknamed the St Kildans the 'bird people' for their skills, the cleverest would use a running noose attached to a cane.

During the 19th century the numbers of birds killed dropped to around 5,000 gannets, 12,000 fulmars and 20 to 25,000 puffins a year. By the 20th century, the islanders depended far less on birds for food. And since the islanders left St Kilda for new homes on the mainland, seabird numbers have increased dramatically. As soon as their experiments were set up, the scientists began to realize their expectations were not going to be fulfilled. The puffins on St Kilda, miles from any industry, were full of heavy metals. They contained even more metals than those on the Isle of May, who, as expected, contained fairly large quantities. And neither of the puffin colonies appeared to be suffering any harm. On the contrary, both colonies were thriving.

Heavy metals like cadmium and mercury are elements. They occur naturally in rocks all over the world, particularly at sea. They get into the environment in many ways, often through erosion or weathering, sometimes as a result of volcanic eruptions in the earth's crust on the sea bed. In northern Spain the ore of mercury, cinnabar, can be seen running red in the rivers. Various industrial processes add to concentrations of these metals: aluminium and zinc smelting particularly release large quantities of cadmium into the environment. Mercury is also used for refining precious metals. It had been thought that industrial production far outweighed natural input; estimates put the figures at 152,046 tons from industry during 1970–78 against 40 tons a year by natural processes. But as a result of the puffin study, this view is changing and the bulk of heavy metal pollution is thought to come from natural sources.

Discoveries like this are changing our perception of what we call pollution. Widely held prejudices about the impact of industry on wildlife and the environment are having to be revised. Scientists are realizing that the natural world produces its own deadly poisons, many of them as pernicious as any man has been able to manufacture. The natural world is a dangerous enough place without even taking man into account. But wildlife seems to survive. The most interesting thing to come out of the seabird study was an explanation of how they cope.

Analysis of the birds' livers and kidneys showed they had been damaged by the heavy metals. But close inspection revealed the damage was continuously under repair. The birds had a special protein called metallothionein, which seemed to be constantly in operation, allowing tissue repair mechanisms time to do their job. It meant, in essence, that the seabirds were equipped to deal with the range of poisons they might reasonably be expected to meet in their environment.

Discoveries such as this have revolutionized the way we think about our wildlife. During the pesticide tragedies, we marvelled at the intricacy and complexity of ecosystems and heeded the dire warning of the peregrine. Now we are learning new respect, for it seems wildlife is cleverer than we thought. Not only does the natural world produce the most deadly poisons, it produces mechanisms for dealing with them.

The seabirds' metallothionein is now being developed as an early warning system. It is one of at least 30 'stress proteins' identified in a range of cells and

A grey seal pup. There is a great deal of concern about the possible effects of industrial pollution on these loveable creatures.

organisms from bacteria to people. Scientists believe these proteins can provide a very sensitive indicator of environmental stress. Industries could use organisms which produce the proteins to monitor pollution, for instance, of waterways near factories. The nature of the protein produced will identify the contamination, while the amount will indicate the severity.

A simple variation of this mechanism is already well developed. For some years scientists from the Plymouth Marine Laboratory have been travelling the world looking at mussel banks. The physiology of the mussel is well understood and its virtue of staying put makes it an ideal indicator of pollution at sea. Detailed analysis of the mussel's reaction to a range of pollutants has been catalogued and can now be used to identify the cause of the contamination.

Even the Norfolk reed, it seems, can teach us a thing or two, about cleaning up our own mess. *Phragmites Australis,* its Latin name, has been in demand for centuries for thatching. Now it is taking on a much more hi-tech role. In the village of Acle, Anglia Water Authority have planted two very special reed beds. Built on a carefully measured slope in a gravel base, they are cheaply, safely and efficiently performing an essential function: treating the sewage from half the population of the village.

The bed at Acle is one of 23 experimental reed beds set up all over the country under the auspices of the Water Research Centre. The treatment is the brainchild of a German scientist and is wonderfully simple – in principle.

Phragmites can grow in soils without oxygen. The reed sucks in oxygen through little holes in its leaves called stomata. The oxygen passes through the leaf sheaths or channels and a pressure builds up inside the plant. A convective flow develops which pushes the oxygen down the stem and out through the rhizomes, or roots. Bacteria living on the roots and in the surrounding soil then act on the sewage and break it down into harmless substances. For instance, the bacteria oxidize ammonium compounds in the sewage to nitrates and then the nitrates are further reduced by other bacteria into atmospheric nitrogen. This same process of oxidization enables the reed to deal with heavy metals too. Iron, where it is naturally present in the soil, becomes harmless iron oxide in the reed bed. Once oxidized, a toxin is insoluble and cannot therefore be taken up by plants.

High hopes are now pinned on this particular aspect of the reed's detoxifying abilities by a variety of industries, including British Coal Open Cast, British Steel and ICI. ICI are hoping to treat toxic waste from their Billingham fertilizer works on Teesside.

If the reed beds take off in the future, they could play an important part in conservation of habitat for a range of wildlife not easily accommodated elsewhere. Reed beds are a wonderful habitat for wildlife, but those in Britain had lost their economic use and were in danger of declining. A new use for the reed in controlling sewage and industrial waste would preserve this habitat for reed warblers, reed buntings and many other birds. It is an exciting prospect. So often the natural world is regarded as a victim, with no defences of its own. Industrialism always threatens to destroy it, but it does not easily accept defeat.

6 Acid Tests

Adolf Hitler, preparing for an invasion of Britain at the outbreak of the last war, unwittingly provided a picture of what the landscape of eastern England was like half a century ago which has proved to be of great value to botanists. The Luftwaffe, equipped with high quality plate cameras, flew several missions over East Anglia and brought back a unique photographic record. These photographs have ended up in the US National Archives in Virginia where an historian of the British countryside unearthed them.

The pictures are detailed enough to show individual houses and streets and the Luftwaffe recorded the existence of a number of strange, shanty town settlements in Essex. These were the plotlands, the self-built homes of East Londoners who, earlier this century and during the 1920s, colonized the Essex countryside. Land was cheap here because of the agricultural depression and families would buy plots for very little, camp on them at weekends, and gradually built themselves a rural idyll. The planners of the 1930s hated these frontier settlements and had them outlawed, so that many were abandoned. Basildon New Town was built on the site of one of the largest plotland settlements.

Hitler's photographic record is invaluable evidence now for what was there in 1939, for you can take with you one of the Luftwaffe's carefully referenced snaps and compare the aerial view with what is on the ground today. In many cases, where there were houses and streets or fields, there is woodland. Although most of the trees are only 40 years old or so, they are a decent size and in many cases they are oak and not the classic colonizing varieties such as birch.

With the guidance of Oliver Rackham the botanist, who has become the high priest of woodland history in Britain, you can make out many layers in these new or secondary woods. Here is wide-girthed oak maybe 200 years old which would have stood in a hedgerow before the plotland settlement was built. Acorns from this and other oaks would have provided the seed for the new woodland around. Within the wood which grows on the plotland there is an old pear tree, a back garden survivor. And then a great earth bank running through the wood which, to the tutored eye, is a clear boundary line. Ancient woods were mostly protected by earth banks, and, sure enough, as you cross this border, the oak trees give way to quite a different kind of wood.

This other wood looks, at first glance, younger than the oak wood for many of the trees have stems only wrist-thick, and they sprout from the ground like the frame of a basket. These are, in fact, very old hornbeam trees which were coppiced for fuel until only twenty or thirty years ago. The stump from which the coppice shoots grow is ancient, gnarled and wide. In spring bluebells grow in the ancient wood, but not yet in the new oak wood.

Without a knowledge of history, you might easily walk through these trees and notice none of this – it would all just be one wood of an indeterminate age. And without a special ecological study of the species found in the different parts of the wood, it would be impossible to say how the old and new woods differ. But the assumption would be that the old wood was better for wildlife, simply because of its age.

OPPOSITE *The bluebell wood, a timeless image of rural England. Though ancient woods have been disappearing since the last war, there is more woodland in Britain now than a century ago.*

There is, in modern conservation, a strong antiquarian theme – a belief that something which has been around a long time, undisturbed, is more valuable to wildlife than a similar habitat which is newly arisen. Or rather that you simply cannot recreate ancient habitats – once they have gone, it will take thousands of years for them to return, and even then, they will not truly replicate what has been lost.

So there is a tendency to despise the newly-established wood and to dismiss as poor quality those habitats which have become established in the wake of human endeavour or destruction. Gravel pits are not really like ancient wetlands; scrubland is not as good as an old hedgerow that has been grubbed up; suburban gardens attract only boringly familiar kinds of wildlife; heathlands preserved on golf courses are not like the real old heathlands that are fast disappearing.

This fashionable view that wildlife is a kind of fixed resource which is being fast eroded by rearrangements of the landscape – the building of motorways or new suburban housing – is inevitably very gloomy. The proposed routes of new roads always pass through two or three supposedly irreplaceable Sites of Special Scientific Interest. New housing is always being built on the last remnant of some lowland heath which is the only surviving refuge of some creature that most people have never seen or even heard of but is said to be in terrible danger of extinction in Britain.

The truth is only rarely as stark as that. In most cases the reworking of the landscape over the years has been good for some kinds of wildlife and not for others. Some species, like the blackbird, have done very well and are found everywhere, while others, like the natterjack toad, are confined by their lifestyle to only a few places and could easily be wiped out. Understandably, the rarest and most vulnerable plants and creatures are valued more highly than those which have remained, or become, common. But there is a great deal of badly defined and ill-researched conservationist scaremongering going on.

In reality, the component parts of the landscape can be continuously rearranged without disastrous effects for wildlife, chiefly because the ability to colonize new ground is a built-in evolutionary mechanism which all successful plants and animals have. For the most part, plants and animals cannot make rapid and significant changes to the way in which they behave – ground-nesting birds continue to nest on the ground – and if their habitat is destroyed they have to find a replacement elsewhere.

A neat way of studying this problem is to compare the kinds of wildlife that lived in an area of farmland with the range of species that takes over or survives when new housing is built on the fields. Very few such case histories exist, but there is an account not yet published of what happened when an area of farmland in Cambridgeshire was turned into a new housing estate with light industries, playing fields and a shopping centre. It covers 22 years of change and is a model for the kind of comparison that could be made all over the country.

The study has been a labour of love by the scientist Norman Moore, recently retired from the Nature Conservancy Council, of the area in which he lives. Before the building of Bar Hill began, there were fields of wheat and other cereal crops and the fields were quite extensive. There was a farmhouse, which is still there, and two small woods, one planted in the 19th century and the other a later sweet chestnut plantation. There were hedges between the fields, one of them very ancient and a former parish boundary where bluebells grew. There was a duck decoy pond which had become overgrown.

In other words, it was classical arable farming country, not particularly good for wildlife, but a recognizable and not unpleasant piece of English countryside

OPPOSITE *Despite the great growth of towns, the spread of industry and the building of motorways, 85 per cent of Britain is still rural. Large-scale chemical farming remains the single greatest threat to wildlife – a field of barley in Berkshire is less favourable to most wild plants and animals than a golf course or even a suburban back garden.*

which has been turned into a town with a population of more than 4,000 people. It is a new settlement in a rural area with nostalgic street names such as Fox Hollow, Pheasant Close and Partridge Drive.

The last of these is in fact a memorial, for the partridges that lived on the edges of the cornfields have gone. These are birds which feed on grain in the autumn, which nest in hedgerows and feed their young on insects, cannot survive in suburbia. They have declined all over the country during this century, partly because weedkillers have wiped out the plants which attracted the insects on which they fed their chicks. The hares have disappeared from Bar Hill too, with the coming of the new town. They too need open fields in which to feed and raise their young.

As the town grew, the skylarks which had filled the air with song in summer gradually disappeared. These are ground nesting birds and suburban back gardens and playing fields are no use as a habitat for them. Corn bunting and yellow hammers, the pretty speckled birds which sit in hedgerows and have a song that is supposed to sound like 'a little bit of bread and no cheese,' have gone too.

So quite a bit of familiar wildlife disappeared. But all those birds which, on the farmland, nested in hedgerows and in the woods have remained and some have colonized the new suburban gardens. These include blackbirds, robins, chaffinches, hedge sparrows or dunnocks, blue tits, great tits, long-tailed tits, song thrushes and greenfinches. All of these are familiar garden birds and will eat food put out for them in the autumn and winter. Suburban gardens provide them in time with quite a suitable habitat. In the early years of suburbia, before the gardens are mature many of these birds, like the long tailed tit, remain in the hedges of the old farmland.

The density of the bird population at Bar Hill – measured as the number of individuals recorded per hectare – has actually increased since the town was built. But some species have become particularly dominant: house sparrows, starlings and blackbirds.

There has been only one significant newcomer to the area since the town was built. This is the house martin, which builds a mud nest under the roofs of houses. It is, like the sparrow and the starling, a commensal bird – it has evolved to live in close proximity to man. The other new arrival has been, oddly, the meadow pipit, which behaves rather like the skylark – which has disappeared – but has begun to nest on an allotment site at Bar Hill.

The range of birds has fallen overall, although their absolute numbers have increased. In time this might change, for as the suburban gardens mature they might attract new species.

With the butterflies the story is quite different: their numbers have increased dramatically since Bar Hill was built. The common blue, the Essex skipper and the meadow brown have all done well, particularly on the rough ground of a remaining bit of unfarmed green belt. But the biggest gain has been in the numbers of dragonflies, and the varieties. Eleven new species have colonized the area, some in water in a small hollow created as a flood control measure for the town, and others – the majority – on the pond dug out for the local golf course.

The golf course pond has also attracted, though it is not yet mature, coots and tufted duck, both of which have done very well on gravel pits and other man-made lakes. The small woods at Bar Hill were not destroyed by the building of the town and have been preserved as an attractive feature of the area so that an important part of the landscape has been preserved. The preservation of much of the countryside around Bar Hill as 'amenity' for the new residents has obviously been important for the survival of many species in the short term.

Wherever suburbia is built, there will be losses and gains. But for those who are worried about the disappearance of certain relatively rare species, the spread of towns is considered a disaster. If the new town eats into heathland, for example, there is little likelihood that the snakes and lizards will survive in back gardens, while the birds and hedgehogs and foxes that move in are already plentiful in the countryside. By recreating over and over again the suburban savannah of lawns, shrubs, flower beds and small trees, we are destroying the diversity of habitat in the country.

There is always a danger of this happening, for virtually the whole of the British landscape has a use which has evolved throughout history. Heathland is disappearing, as we have seen, because it is no longer a valuable part of the countryside – nobody grazes animals or gathers fuel there any more.

However, it is nearly always the case that somewhere, somehow, a new use is found for a similar kind of habitat. In the case of heathland, there has been occupation by the Army since the mid-19th century which has preserved some of it. And, along with the suburban way of life, another demand has arisen – for golf courses.

Golf evolved as a game on the wild sand dune grasslands of eastern Scotland, and in its early form was played across country. The familiar golf course is a regulated version of that and in its landscaping some of the features of the terrain in which it evolved are retained – the rough, sandpits, small ponds and so on – which in the game are obstacles to the golfer, but for wildlife are most attractive areas.

The hedgehog, once persecuted by gamekeepers, and still a frequent casualty on roads, is thriving in Britain. Golf courses and suburban gardens provide it with ideal habitat.

OPPOSITE *Though many golf courses are an artificial recreation of coastal sandy links, a great deal of wildlife like the kestrel is able to exploit them. About 60 per cent of most golf courses is 'rough' – heathland and woodland – and valuable habitat in a landscape that modern farming has made hostile.*

Since golf first became popular at the end of the 19th century, the number of courses has been growing steadily and there are now around 3,000 in Great Britain. The creation of new courses is, in effect, a way of re-introducing areas of grassland and heathland to parts of the country where there was none before, or at least of preserving remaining patches which are made part of the course. In recent years the amount of land occupied by golf courses has increased very fast, chiefly through the enlargement of those already established. More than 80 per cent of the new terrain taken over was previously used for arable farming.

So alongside the development of suburbia, the rise of the golf course does promise to provide a place for those species which are never likely to colonize little back gardens in Partridge Drive, Fox Hollow, or Pheasant Close. Such birds as yellowhammers and skylarks which are pushed out by the new town might do well on the golf course, which could also provide a suitable habitat for snakes, lizards and butterflies, which are confined to smaller and smaller islands of surviving heathland.

RIGHT *A young tawny owl, a successful exploiter of the ever changing landscape of Britain.*

One of the rarest creatures in Britain, the sand lizard finds a home on the sandy links of Royal Birkdale golf course on the Lancashire coast. In the breeding season the male lizard is a brilliant emerald green.

For the most part, golf courses have been created on sand dunes, heathlands and grasslands and, in this sense, have simply occupied valuable wildlife areas. They have not created them from scratch. The laying out of the courses with fairways and manicured greens has inevitably destroyed some of the best existing wildlife areas. But it is now generally agreed that, if it had not been for the popularity of golf, many of these otherwise worthless areas would have disappeared much faster than they have.

At Royal Birkdale Golf Course, on the sand dunes of the Lancashire coast, some of the rarest of Britain's wild creatures survive alongside some of the most celebrated golfers at international tournaments. There are natterjack toads here, and the brilliant emerald green sand lizard. Sand lizards not only need sandy soil in which to lay their eggs. It seems they regulate their body temperatures by moving between the shade of small shrubs and open ground, and the scrub plants of the sand dunes provide them with this variety of warmth and shady cool.

It is likely that the sand lizards at Royal Birkdale were isolated there several thousand years ago by climatic change. A period of warm weather encouraged them to move north in England but a cooling 5,000 years ago forced them to retreat except on those patches of sand dune which were especially warm and favourable. Both natterjack toads and sand lizards are otherwise confined to the heathlands and sand dunes of southern England, and it is something of an anomaly that there should be such valuable colonies so far north.

The isolation of these reptiles on and around the dunes of Royal Birkdale emphasizes one of the most critical factors for the survival of wildlife in a landscape which is changing as fast as that in Britain. If a suitable habitat were created for them in, say, Leicestershire, there would be no prospect of them reaching it if they were not deliberately introduced by conservationists. Unlike many other creatures such as birds, they have no means to disperse over wide areas of the country. And, as the places in which they can survive become smaller and more isolated from each other, the whole population becomes more vulnerable. Where heathlands which were once great continuous tracts of waste are broken up into pockets, extinction takes place piecemeal. First the sand lizards disappear from one patch, and then another, and the distance between surviving colonies is too great for them to reclaim the lost territory.

This is one reason why species with very exacting requirements in terms of habitat are particularly vulnerable in the evolving landscape of the country, while the great mass of wildlife is able to stay on the move and cope with the continual rearrangement of woodland, freshwater, heathland, grassland and so on. And it is one of the main justifications conservationists have for opposing any change in sensitive parts of the landscape. While much of it can happily be rearranged like a jigsaw puzzle, some critical bits are always liable to disappear.

An understanding of the intricacies of the behaviour of wildlife is historically very recent. Modern ecology did not really evolve until the 1920s, and since then a great deal of painstaking and ingenious scientific investigation has revealed how vulnerable some plants and animals are. This has given rise to a tremendous sensitivity to any plans to disturb the landscape, for the ecological effects can be imagined.

But scientific understanding has also begun to undermine some of the most cherished beliefs of conservationists about the nature of the landscape they wish to preserve. The assumption, for example, that there is such a thing as pristine, natural wilderness has been repeatedly questioned. One of the first shocks was the discovery that the Norfolk Broads were the result of 14th century peat digging – a revelation of research in the 1960s.

With the aid of new techniques, botanists have been delving into the history of the very soil of Britain and painting a picture of the past which is in many ways surprising. What it emphasizes is how much even the most venerable bits of landscape and most gnarled and ancient woods are evidence of previous human endeavour as much as the work of nature.

The great symbol of ancient countryside in England is the oak tree. For a very long time it was assumed that the country was covered in oakwood, with birch, pine, ash, hazel, lime and other broadleaved trees surviving in pockets where the oak did not grow. Only in Scotland, and on the uplands, was the natural forest of pine. In broad terms, Britain was described as having originally an oakwood 'climax' community of species.

By climax is meant a relatively stable community of plants which had evolved since the retreat of the glaciers, with a succession of invading trees like birch gradually being pushed out as the oaks took root and began to shade out the ground beneath them. But this idea of the oak climax community has now been seriously challenged.

An attempt has been made to map the kinds of tree that were dominant 5,000 years ago by analysing pollen grains buried for millennia in the soil. Pollen grains are tiny and very durable and sufficiently distinct when seen under a microscope for the plant which produced them to be identified. Samples of soil are taken using an aluminium tube called a Livingstone Corer which is pushed into a piece

OVERLEAF *The sickly sea of yellow rape symbolizes agribusiness in modern Britain – some wildlife like woodpigeons thrive on it but many creatures which find a refuge in abandoned industrial areas are driven out by this kind of monoculture.*

of ground which has remained undisturbed – the sediment in a lake, for example. The pollen is laid down in chronological layers and is separated from the soil by an elaborate purification process. By counting pollen grains on a slide you can tell which were the dominant species in that bit of mud.

To find the age of the mud, another process is needed called radiocarbon dating. The world is full of an isotope of carbon which is radioactive. It enters the atmosphere from exploding stars and forms little particles which react with the nitrogen gas in the air to form carbon 14 – radioactive carbon. This gets mixed with the carbon dioxide in the atmosphere and is absorbed by plants in the process of photosynthesis. Carbon 14 ends up in the soil. Once it is lodged there, it begins to break down in a series of spontaneous eruptions, but it takes a very long time to disappear. Its half-life – the time it takes for half of it to disappear – is 5,500 years. So, by measuring the energy level left in carbon 14

One of the greatest threats to the natural world in Britain today is the atmospheric pollution from industry which produces 'greenhouse' gases and acid rain.

in a sample of soil, scientists can calculate how old it is.

This very involved process has been repeated many times for soil samples and other relics such as mammoth teeth. It has provided a picture of which plants were around long before any human records were made. Some of the results are quite surprising.

Oak woodland did not predominate in lowland England back in 5000 BC – it was relatively rare. The most common tree in this region appears to have been the small-leaved lime, a different species from the lime trees that grow in the streets of many of our cities. Over the north of England, west Wales and in the south-west, the oak was the dominant tree of the forests. Around the Wash there were extensive tracts of alder, and ash forests in parts of East Anglia.

A good deal of guesswork has gone into the maps produced because the number and distribution of soil samples could not cover the whole country. Adjustment has also been made for the fact that different species of tree produce different quantities of pollen – oak has much more than small-leaved lime, for example. But the evidence is at least sufficient to cast serious doubt on the assumption that the oak was the natural woodland tree of England, and to suggest that the predominance of oak within recorded history is artificial. Many of the ancient oak woods were planted to provide timber, firewood, acorns and bark which was essential for the tanning of leather until synthetic materials were found in the 19th century.

Ancient oakwoods are often survivals of an early form of monoculture – the planting of a single crop over a wide area. So too are the beech woods of the Chiltern hills. The evidence of the pollen grains is that the wildwood of Britain was quite mixed, just as the rain forests are today.

The new woods like those that have grown since the last war on the old plotlands of Essex do not follow the rules laid down by textbooks. You would expect the first trees to take root to be birch and for there to be a succession leading eventually, after maybe two or three hundred years, to oak and hornbeam woods. But quite often the new woods are predominantly oak from the very beginning. In the Chilterns, where the old beech trees are dying, their enormous branches snapping and crashing to the ground, oak saplings are invading. And the oaks appear to grow surprisingly quickly for a hardwood tree – after 40 years or so they are quite substantial, with the kind of trunk you can easily wrap your arms around but which you cannot bend or even shake.

In many woods too which were clear-felled and then planted with conifers when that was the vogue with foresters earlier this century, the pines are dying and the broad-leaved woodland is coming back. The overall impression is of incredible vigour.

It is, therefore, a tremendous shock to learn from some conservationist groups such as Friends of the Earth that all the trees in Britain are not rudely healthy and irrepressible, but are slowly dying. A recent survey suggested that 90 per cent of British trees were suffering from the effects of acid rain. This alarming statistic was backed up by another study by the Forestry Commission, which until recently had rejected the idea that in Britain acid rain was a problem. Such pronouncements flatly contradict what we see with our eyes, which makes them all the more disturbing. The natural vigour of the plant-life of the country, it is said, must be an illusion.

What the fears about acid rain express is a final condemnation of industrialism. It may have had many fortuitous and unforeseen effects which have actually been useful for wildlife, but, in the end, it will get us for the very atmosphere has been poisoned by the essential force which drives industrialism – power.

As we saw in the last chapter, acid rain was known about and studied in detail in the 19th century. Locally it was devastating then, particularly the emissions from alkali works which doused the surrounding countryside in hydrochloric acid and killed crops and wild plants alike. The pollution of cities by smoke became a major public health issue in Victorian England which was not effectively tackled until the 1950s when the burning of coal was banned. Atmospheric filth was then quite tangible in a way it is not today: in London and other large cities, the bark and leaves of trees were black with soot in the summer. At Kew Gardens many trees would not grow and had to be removed to a safer spot outside the city.

The threat of acid rain today is much less obvious. In Europe it has affected first those regions where the soil and water are naturally acid anyway and which are vulnerable because prevailing winds have carried the sulphur and nitrogen from power stations and industrial plants all over the continent to the north.

In Sweden many lakes have gone biologically dead, and the only temporary solution that has been found is the absurd and frightening one of dumping lime into them from aeroplanes.

Nothing so dramatic has yet happened in Britain, but there are research programmes now which are discovering that in the clouds there are chemicals which are altering the ecology of rivers, heathlands and woodlands. But the picture scientists are putting together is in many ways surprising and contradictory.

High on the fells of Cumbria there is a most bizarre research station clustered around a radar tracker that looks like a giant golf ball. Here a team from the Institute of Terrestrial Ecology is engaged in catching and analysing clouds. The moorland around is completely devoid of trees – not because of acid rain now or in the past, but because of soil erosion which came about centuries ago when the original woodland was destroyed and the land turned over to sheep grazing. The peat is acid and the landscape beautifully gaunt, the summer colours of heather and wiry grass like a patchwork quilt as the sun and cloud shadow plays on it.

The key piece of equipment used on Great Dunn Fell is incredibly simple – a few strands of thread which catch moisture so that it rolls down into a plastic container. According to the wind direction, the clouds have blown across the Atlantic or from Europe. The samples of cloud vary considerably. Some are quite clean, others like ink – the white cloud turns to black liquid in the collecting bottle.

There is acid in these clouds all right, the sulphur and nitrogen fumes from power stations having mixed with droplets of moisture in the atmosphere. And there is little doubt that this is having an effect on the plant life not only of the Cumbrian moors but places much further away.

In a valley in Wales another team of researchers is studying the breeding success of a charming little bird called the dipper. It lives on fast-flowing streams which tumble, tea-brown, through wooded valleys. The dipper is a plump little bird with a white bib, so that it is reminiscent of a waiter. It is often seen standing on stones in the white froth of the water, bobbing up and down and piping excitedly. When it flies off it skims low over the water, following the line of the stream.

A remarkable ability of the dipper is to walk under water. It ducks below the surface and then emerges again as if it had some special ability to resist the force of the current. Much of its food is found amongst the polished pebbles of these clear streams. These are little crustacea adapted to live in the acid water. But if the stream becomes too acid, the dipper's food supply begins to dwindle, and it needs to establish a much larger territory in order to breed. This is what appears

OPPOSITE *The dipper, which has the remarkable ability to walk under water in search of its food, has been badly affected in some places by increasing acidity in the water which kills the larvae on which dippers feed.*

Rivers like this in the Welsh mountains tend to be naturally acid because of the underlying rock and are especially vulnerable to the increased acidity from the planting of conifers and atmospheric pollution.

to have been happening with the dippers in Wales, and quite possibly in other parts of Britain such as the Highlands of Scotland. It is quite an alarming and, at first, unbelievable prospect that the cumulative emissions from power stations and factories should be destroying the food supply of these little birds.

As always, the science is not yet entirely clear, for there is another reason the rivers have become acid. This is the planting of the barren uplands with conifers. In precisely those regions where acid rainfall is a problem, the re-afforestation with alien sitka spruce and other fast-growing, supposedly quick return pines has been going on. These plantations produce an acid run-off which affects the streams of the hills. So the dipper is subject to a two-pronged attack.

The conifer plantations themselves are liable to attack from acid rain which, in Germany and parts of Scandinavia, has been devastating. It seems that here, in the remotest places, the effects of industrialism are biting first. This is not entirely illogical, for the efforts to free the more populated and built-up areas of atmospheric pollution has led to the construction of higher chimneys and cooling towers which carry the chemical pollutants higher and further away in the wind.

Whereas in the 19th century they would blight the area immediately around a town or factory, now they become part of the composition of the clouds.

These acid clouds do not affect all parts of the country – or other countries for that matter – equally. Where the clouds actually come down over the hills, the change in the chemical composition of the soil is likely to be most dramatic. But the results are not always predictable.

One of the most devastating effects of man's activities on the soil of Britain has been the enriching of it with fertilizers. This can be disastrous for wild flowers which are adapted to thrive on earth which is very poor in nutrients. A good example of this is the sundew. This is a heathland plant which has solved the problem of surviving on badly eroded and infertile soil by catching its nutrients in the air. It has sticky buds which trap flies and slowly digest them. If the heathland soil becomes enriched, the sundew itself dies. One of the startling results of the recent studies on acid rain is that the nitrogen in it fertilizes the soil, inhibiting the growth of typical heathland plants and encouraging the regeneration of woodland.

At one and the same time, depending on where it falls, acid rain can damage trees or encourage their growth. Sometimes it does both. The subtleties of this are currently being studied in a series of especially constructed greenhouses at an Institute of Terrestrial Ecology research station near Edinburgh. Miniature trees are coated with sprays containing different mixes of chemicals common in clouds. Some species, like the lodge pole pine, may actually thrive on the increased nutrients in the mix. Most trees, however, though they may appear to remain healthy in the summer, show weaknesses such as vulnerability to frost damage. The degree to which they survive pollution may, therefore, depend on the weather – a cold winter could severely harm them though they might thrive in warm conditions.

And, of course, the very same gases which are implicated in the formation of acid rain have another effect on the functioning of the plant which in the last few years has become a popular catch-phrase of conservationist fears – the greenhouse effect.

The greenhouse effect is spoken of, and written about, as if it were a very new and pernicious result of human activity, the burning of fossil fuels to power industrialism. In fact, it is essential to life on earth – without it the planet would be too cold for life. It is an entirely natural phenomenon which has, in recent years, been affected by human activity.

During the billions of years in which the earth has been evolving, the intensity of heat from the sun has been rising. The temperature at the earth's surface has, however, remained remarkably constant and at a level which has made life possible. The regulating mechanism is the generation of carbon dioxide. This is in contrast to two other planets which scientists have investigated in detail in the hope of discovering whether or not they could have, or have had, life. One is Venus, which developed so much carbon dioxide in its atmosphere that it is much too hot for life – temperatures average 460 degrees Centigrade. The other is Mars which is much too cold because it lacks carbon dioxide and shivers at minus 60 degrees Centigrade. The earth has had just about the right amount of carbon dioxide, the principal 'greenhouse' gas, and would average 35 degrees Centigrade cooler without it.

Carbon dioxide, as well as water vapour and some other gases, has a warming effect because it allows through some of the sun's most energy-charged light rays, but prevents the irradiated reflected heat from the earth's surface from escaping. It is a bit like the glass panes in a greenhouse which trap the sun and

produce artificially warm conditions in which plants grow vigorously.

How it is that the earth has maintained a pretty even temperature for so many millenia remains something of a mystery. It is known that the end of the last Ice Age was associated with a big increase in carbon dioxide in the atmosphere, and this has given rise to the fear that the amount industrial nations are pumping into the atmosphere will similarly warm the climate. But, in geological history, it must have been the case that the planet has had some regulatory mechanism for adjusting to sudden increases in carbon dioxide, for this can come about quite naturally with an increase in volcanic activity.

Whether or not there is a mechanism whereby the plant life of the earth will be able to absorb the excess of carbon dioxide which is now being produced is a matter of fierce dispute in scientific circles. Before industrialism, the long-term trend was for carbon dioxide to *fall* in the atmosphere, which would be equally disastrous for existing life forms because it is an essential gas in the process of photosynthesis whereby green plants convert the sun's energy into food for other creatures. New plants are evolving which need less carbon dioxide.

The big question is whether or not industrialism has, or is about to, upset the tenuous balance of chemistry which makes life on earth possible. Ozone is the most fearful term in this context. More than the horrors of greenhouse warming or acid rain pollution, the prospect of apparently innocent aerosol cans and refrigerators producing invisible particles which eat away at a protective layer around the world has captured the popular imagination and provided the most telling evidence that, in the end, industrialism will get us. The problem of ozone depletion is especially poignant because the wealthier nations are able quickly to adjust to the problem while the Third World threatens to destroy everything as it tries to keep pace industrially.

Whereas nobody but the experts had heard of chlorofluorocarbons (CFCs) when they were first used as an alternative to ammonia in refrigeration or in aerosol cans, now that they are a threat they have become a household term. The fact that they hang about in the air and rise to the stratosphere where they destroy ozone, which acts as a protection against the more pernicious of the sun's rays, was a terrible revelation, and introduced the great mass of people to the existence and importance of this phenomenon.

Ozone in the stratosphere is a good thing. Ozone, created by the action of the sun on petrol fumes in the atmosphere, is a very bad thing, the main constituent of poisonous fogs. Like most chemicals, ozone is essentially neither good nor bad: it depends where it is, what it is doing and how much of it there is. The same is true with carbon dioxide and acid in rain.

It is the most contentious axiom of green philosophy that natural things are good, and things which are the creation of human industrial activity are bad. A great many natural things such as volcanoes, viruses and diseases are very bad for people. And a great many industrial things are very good for people. They are also good for many kinds of wildlife.

The essential proposition of this book, and the television series it accompanies, is that if you believe industrialism in all its manifestations to be intrinsically bad for the natural world, then you will not be able to explain how and why it has responded as it has over the past two centuries. The good effects, however unexpected and unintended they may have been, are as striking as the bad effects. In fact, they are more telling simply because they are so unexpected, given the prejudices most of us have.

Despite the pollution of rivers, the kingfisher manages to survive in modern Britain. There are thought to be about 5,000 breeding pairs today.

It is impossible to understand separately the nastiness of industrialism and its beneficial effects. All the science which now is used to condemn as destructive our industrial society would be quite impossible without it – it is dependent on coal, electricity, chemicals, computers, petrol, the mining and smelting of metals. And the very sensibility which underlies the impulse to conservation is a product of the degree of command over the world that industrial developments have given us.

In the end, the acid test will be whether or not industrialism generates the means, through science and political awareness, to control its own destructiveness. The rapidity with which the wealthier nations have responded to the thinning of the ozone layer by banning CFCs is at least promising.

In the meantime, Britain, the first industrial nation, is enjoying in a great many respects a wildlife revival.

Primroses, evocative of the English spring, were decimated in the Victorian era by townspeople who picked them in vast numbers. Special 'primrose' trains were run from the cities to the countryside. Picking primroses, and other wild flowers, is now illegal.

FURTHER READING

In its scope and approach, probably the nearest thing to a textbook on the subject of wildlife and industrial change is Oliver Rackham's *A History of the Countryside.* Like all his books, such as the classic *Ancient Woodland,* it is packed with fascinating material, although the organisation of it is a little eccentric. On industrial archaeology, Barrie Trinder's *The Making of the Industrial Landscape* is a lively guide to the ruins of long lost furnaces, factories and manufacturing centres. *The Ark in our Midst* by Richard Fitter is an excellent guide to introduced species, though a bit out of date now. Christopher Lever's *The Naturalized Animals of the British Isles* is also highly informative.

On fox hunting, Raymond Carr's *English Foxhunting* is the classic, though the more recent study *Peculiar Privilege* by D. C. Itzkowitz is a briefer and very readable alternative. Alwynne Wheeler's *The Tidal Thames* is a classic study in historical ecology, and David Elton's *The Ecology of Invasions* is a fascinating account of the consequences of shipping wildlife around the world and of changes in the environment.

Richard Mabey's *The Common Ground* is a standard work now on conservation issues. James Lovelock's *Gaia,* although very controversial in its thesis, is a brilliant introduction to the subject of planetary chemistry. A classic study of scientific detective work is Derek Ratcliffe's *The Peregrine Falcon,* which is optimistic or pessimistic about the future of wildlife in the chemical age according to the way you look at it.

INDEX

Page numbers in *italics* refer to illustrations

(Endpaper) *The baize carpet in the foreground looks like shingle. In fact it is a mass of knots, wading birds, which have joined oyster catchers at a massive roost on the lagoons at Snettisham in Norfolk. It is a spectacular example of the natural world's exploitation of a landscape forged by human endeavour and the elemental forces of environment.*